The Electrical Plan Reading Workbook
By Tom Henry

While every precaution has been taken in the preparation of this book, the author and publisher assumes no responsibility for errors or omissions. Neither is any liability assumed from the use of the information contained herein.

National Electrical Code® and NEC® are Registered Trademarks of the National Fire Protection Association, Inc., Quincy, MA.

First printing July 1994.

D1591416

ISBN 0 - 945495 - 42 - 0

CONTENTS

ELECTRICAL PLAN READING

Electrical diagrams are the plans and drawings you will use throughout your electrical career.

The plans are the roadmap of the work to be done. Persons unfamiliar with the symbols and specifications find the plans difficult to follow. An experienced electrician will actually make his own plans for certain jobs.

The electrician must have a working knowledge of the elements of building construction, the ability to interpret electrical, mechanical and architectural drawings. The ability to visualize the entire building structure and its relationship to the electrical system is an asset.

There are three types of diagrams the electrician must be able to read: (1) schematic diagrams, (2) pictorial diagrams, and (3) electrical blue prints.

Schematic diagrams are useful for circuit operation or discussing theory, but they are not very useful in building construction. Schematic diagrams won't show the physical layout or location of the components required in construction.

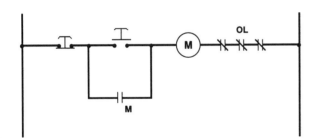

Schematics are used in control circuits. They are read from left to right, from top to bottom.

Construction requires diagrams that show the layout, physical location, and mechanical details.

Pictorial diagrams clearly show the components and how they are actually connected like a photograph of the wiring. Pictorial diagrams are not used for construction purposes.

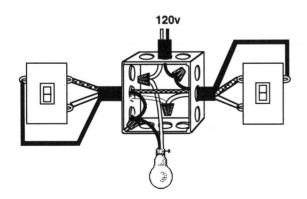

Pictorial diagrams are useful for illustrating portions of a larger wiring diagram.

1

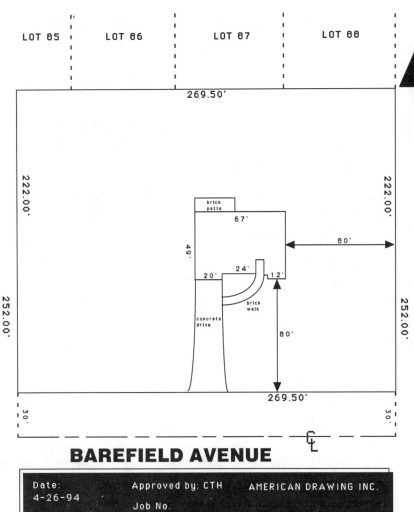

LOT 85   LOT 86   LOT 87   LOT 88

N

269.50'

222.00'

222.00'

252.00'

252.00'

brick patio

67'

49'

80'

24'

20'

12'

brick walk

concrete drive

80'

30'

30'

269.50'

C L

BAREFIELD AVENUE

Date: 4-26-94

Approved by: CTH

AMERICAN DRAWING INC.

Job No.
CSX-2830

Scale: 1" = 40'

Revised _____

There are many different type plans. The site plan shows how the house is located on the property.

The pictorial drawing shows the perspective of a building.

PERSPECTIVE VIEW OF HOUSE

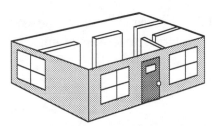

TOP HALF OF HOUSE REMOVED

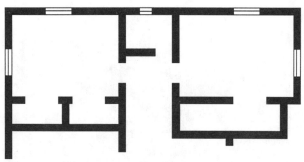

THE FLOOR PLAN IS VIEWING THE HOUSE FROM ABOVE

The wiring diagrams that you will use for constructions jobs are called blueprints. These diagrams use symbols to indicate components and to designate the specifications for various connections.

Blueprints are drawn to scale, the most commonly used are 1/4" = 1 foot or 1/8" = 1 foot.

The blueprint is also called a floor plan in construction as it is a layout of a room, house, or building. A floor plan is a scaled, top view showing inner and outer walls with windows and doors also indicated. No furniture is shown in a floor plan, but major appliances such as ranges, dishwashers, and clothes dryers are shown on some drawings. Most floor plans include the symbols for sinks, toilets and bath tubs. The engineer or architect draws in special symbols representing light fixtures, receptacles, switches, and other components.

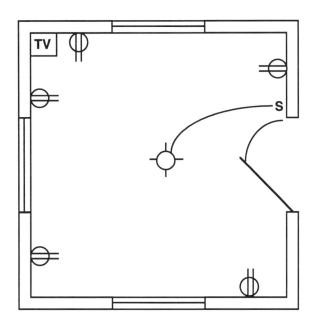

The floor plan does not show how the devices are connected. The electrician is suppose to know how to connect the devices, the electrician's responsibility of reading a blue print is to translate the floor plan into actual electrical wiring.

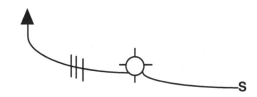

One line diagrams use special symbols for components. The components are shown interconnected by single lines. A single line can represent several wires.

On a one-line diagram, the components, their exact location, and the wiring is shown. These drawings do not show specifications, cable or conduit type, or other supplementary information. This is usually provided on the blueprint in a separate specification box or table.

The two key parts of a blueprint are the symbols used to represent the components and the lines that represent the interconnecting wires.

Abbreviations are used on blueprints to indicate various components or aspects of the job.

ABBREVIATIONS and SYMBOLS

Abbrevations are used in electrical work to indicate various components or other aspects of the job. They can be used in the drawing, the bill of material, the specifications, or other written documents.

PNL = panel **SERV** = service **MTR** = motor **XFMR** = transformer **CKT** = circuit

Symbols are divided into five basic catagories:

1. GENERAL OUTLETS
2. CONVENIENCE RECEPTACLES
3. SWITCHES
4. PANELS, CIRCUITS and MISCELLANEOUS COMPONENTS
5. AUXILIARY SYSTEMS

Sometimes designers of blueprints modify the standard symbols to suit their own needs. For this reason, most drawings will have a symbol list or legend.

General outlet refers to a type of outlet or junction box. It can be for a switch, light fixture, etc. The symbol is a circle around a letter designating the specific type of outlet. The symbol with a short line extending out of the circle on the left side, indicates an outlet that is wall mounted. The symbol without the short line is used for outlets mounted in the wall.

wall   **outlet**

Rectangular symbols are used to represent fluorescent light fixtures. You must also understand what the different letter designations mean. The letters indicated the type of outlet involved. A clock outlet has a "C", a pull switch "S", recessed fixture "R".

fluorescent fixture   **fluorescent fixture recessed**   **clock outlet**   **floodlight with motion detector**

R or ◎ **recessed fixture**   **2-floodlights**   **directional light arrow indicates direction of lamp**   **S** **pull switch**

4

The symbol used for the receptacles is also a circle.

duplex receptacle

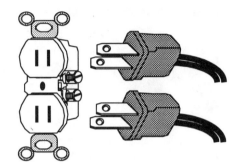

The most popular receptacle used is the duplex receptacle which accepts two cord connections. The symbol is a circle with lines. The lines indicate the type of receptacle: one line = single, two lines = duplex, three lines = triplex.

single receptacle

duplex receptacle

triplex receptacle

Sometimes a duplex receptacle is split so that one outlet is hot while the other outlet is switched. This symbol has a portion of it shaded. A duplex receptacle in the floor is shown in a box.

split-wired duplex

duplex receptacle in floor

end of run (last receptacle)

Special-purpose receptacles have a circle with a triangle in the center. These symbols indicate 240 volt appliance outlets such as ranges, clothes dryers etc. If the triangular portion of the symbol is open, a standard receptacle is indicated. When the triangle is darkened, a special-purpose connection is required. This means that the appliance is normally attached with a special connector rather than with a separate plug and convenience outlet.

single special-purpose receptacle

special-purpose range hood

special-purpose garbage disposal

range receptacle

For switch outlets on a blueprint a large **S** is used. Subscripts are used with the "S" to designate the type of switch required. The everyday common single-pole switch is shown with the letter "S" and no other marking. A three-way switch would have the letter "S" with a subscript "3". A four-way switch would have the letter "S" with a subscript "4".

$$S_3$$

three-way switch

$$S_4$$

four-way switch

The Code defines a lighting and appliance panelboard of one which has more than 10% of its overcurrent devices rated 30 amps or less, for which neutral connections are provided. This would be the case in house wiring, the panelboard would be a lighting panel. In the industry a panelboard with three-phase loads and motors without neutral connections would be an example of a power panel.

branch circuit lighting panel

distribution power panel

Other symbols often used are for motors and instruments. These are circular symbols with letter designations in the center.

motor   **OR**   **motor**

Meters are also designated with a letter symbol to indicate what type of meter.

watthour   **ammeter**   **voltmeter**   **power factor**
meter   **meter**

Lines are used to indicate actual wiring interconnections. A solid straight line represents wiring that is concealed in a wall or ceiling. A line with long, wide dashes or alternating short-and-long dashes is used to represent wiring that is concealed in a floor. A dashed line made up of short dashes is used to represent exposed wiring.

CONCEALED IN   **CONCEALED IN**   **EXPOSED**
WALL OR CEILING   **FLOOR**

The dashed line can represent two things: exposed wires or wires that run between a component and a switch are often used on a blueprint. They are usually shown as a curved dashed line so they are not confused with with architectural details which are represented by straight lines.

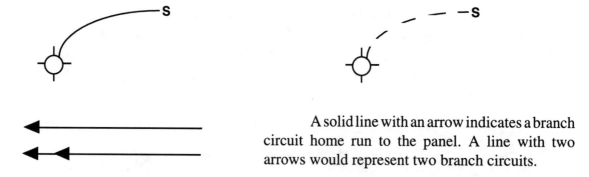

A solid line with an arrow indicates a branch circuit home run to the panel. A line with two arrows would represent two branch circuits.

The slashes in a line represent the number of wires in the cable or conduit. No slashes = one wire, one slash = one wire, two slashes = two wires, three slashes = three wires, etc.

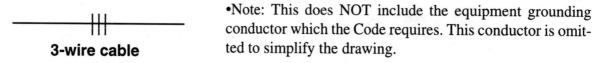

3-wire cable

•Note: This does NOT include the equipment grounding conductor which the Code requires. This conductor is omitted to simplify the drawing.

ELECTRICAL SYMBOLS

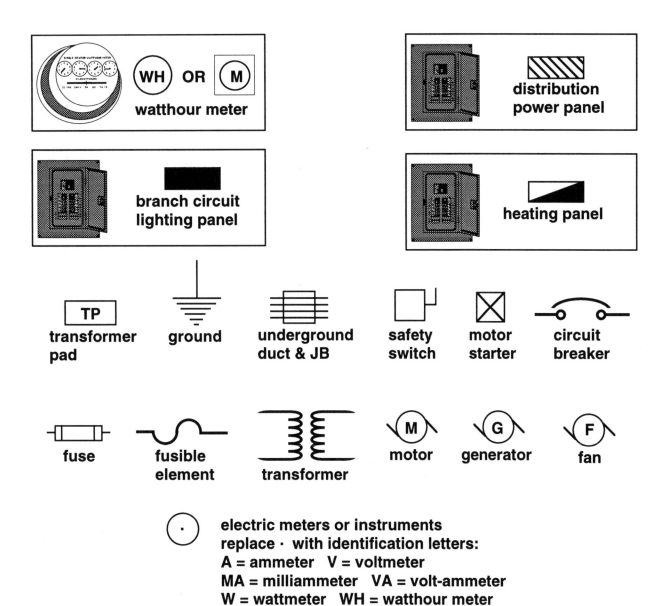

watthour meter

distribution power panel

branch circuit lighting panel

heating panel

TP

transformer pad

ground

underground duct & JB

safety switch

motor starter

circuit breaker

fuse

fusible element

transformer

M motor

G generator

F fan

electric meters or instruments
replace · with identification letters:
A = ammeter V = voltmeter
MA = milliammeter VA = volt-ammeter
W = wattmeter WH = watthour meter
OM = ohmeter PF = power factor

WIRING

WIRING			
NOT CONNECTED	**CONNECTED**	**CONTROL**	**POWER**
HOME RUN	**UNDERGROUND**	**CONCEALED**	**NUMBER OF CIRCUIT CONDUCTORS (4)**

WIRING			
CONCEALED IN CEILING OR WALL	**CONCEALED IN FLOOR**	**EXPOSED**	**WIRING TURNED UP**
WIRING TURNED DOWN	**CONDUIT ONLY**	**CONDUIT TURNED UP**	**CONDUIT TURNED DOWN**
	CO		

ELECTRICAL SYMBOLS

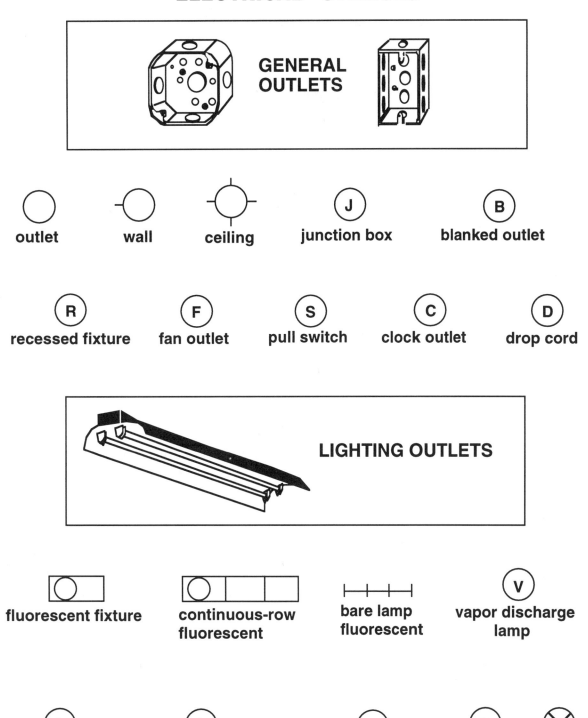

GENERAL OUTLETS

outlet　　wall　　ceiling　　junction box　　blanked outlet

recessed fixture　　fan outlet　　pull switch　　clock outlet　　drop cord

LIGHTING OUTLETS

fluorescent fixture　　continuous-row fluorescent　　bare lamp fluorescent　　vapor discharge lamp

lamp holder　　lamp holder with pull switch　　incandescent　　exit light outlet

ELECTRICAL   SYMBOLS

CONVENIENCE RECEPTACLES

single receptacle

duplex receptacle

triplex receptacle

triplex receptacle 3

quadruplex receptacle

ungrounded duplex receptacle UNG

split-wired duplex

split-wired triplex

single special-purpose receptacle

duplex special-purpose receptacle

range receptacle R

weatherproof receptacle WP

switch and receptacle S

floor receptacle

special-purpose dishwasher DW

special-purpose heat pump HP

special-purpose clothes dryer CD

special-purpose air conditioner AC

ELECTRICAL   SYMBOLS

SWITCHED OUTLETS

S
single-pole switch

S_2
double-pole switch

S_3
three-way switch

S_4
four-way switch

S_D
automatic door switch

S_E
electrolier switch

S_K
key-operated switch

S_P
pilot lamp & switch

S_{CB}
circuit breaker

S_{MC}
momentary switch

S_{MC}
remote control switch

S_{WP}
weatherproof switch

S_{DS}
dimmer switch

S_F
fused switch

S_L
low-voltage switch

S_{LM}
low-voltage master switch

S_T
time switch

ELECTRICAL SYMBOLS

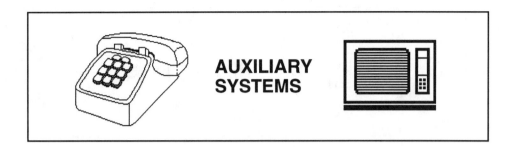

AUXILIARY SYSTEMS

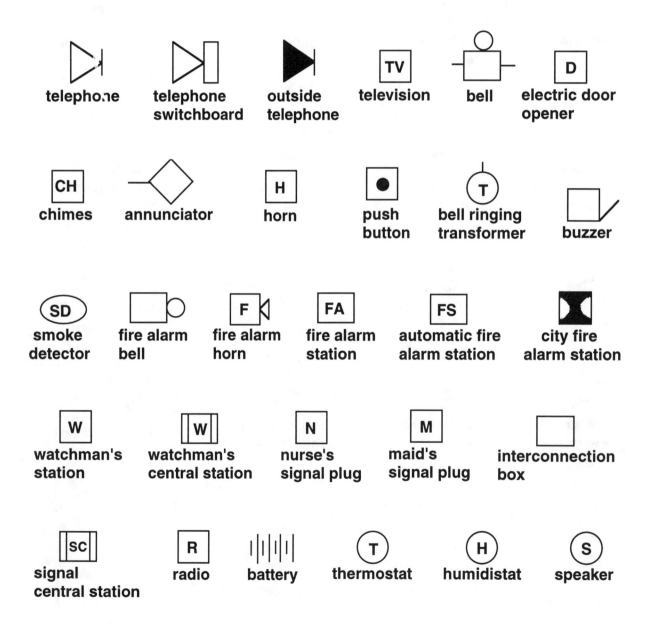

| telephone | telephone switchboard | outside telephone | television | bell | electric door opener |

| chimes | annunciator | horn | push button | bell ringing transformer | buzzer |

| smoke detector | fire alarm bell | fire alarm horn | fire alarm station | automatic fire alarm station | city fire alarm station |

| watchman's station | watchman's central station | nurse's signal plug | maid's signal plug | interconnection box |

| signal central station | radio | battery | thermostat | humidistat | speaker |

13

ABBREVIATIONS

Air Cond.	Air Conditioning	E to E	End to End
AFF	Above Finish Floor	ENT	Entrance
AL	Aluminum	EOR	End Of Run
AC	Alternating current	EP	Explosion Proof
AIC	Ampere Interrupting Capacity	ESP	Emergency Switch Panel
AIR	Ampere Interrupting Rating	EXC	Excavate
APPROX.	Approximate	EXH	Exhaust
ARCH	Architectural	EXIST	Existing
ASPH	Asphalt	EXP JT	Expansion Joint
AV	Average	F	Fan or Fuse
AWG	American Wire Gage	FIN	Finish
BSMT	Basement	FIN. FL	Finish Floor
B	Bathroom	FP	Fire Place
BR	Bedroom	FPRF	Fireproof
BP	Blueprint	FIX	Fixture
BLDG	Building	FL	Flashing, Floor or Flush
BL	Building Line	FLA	Full Load Amps
C	Capacitor	FD	Floor Drain
CAB	Cabinet	FLUOR	Fluorescent
CLG	Ceiling	' or FT	Foot
CEL	Cellar	FTG	Footing
CEM	Cement	FND	Foundation
CTR	Center	FPN	Fine Print Note
C to C	Center to Center	FRM	Frame
CIR or CKT	Circuit	FUR	Future
CL	Center Line	F.B.O.	Furnished By Others
C.B. or CIR BKR	Circuit Breaker	GAR	Garage
CO	Clean Out	GA	Gauge
C, CL or CLO	Closet	GD	Garbage Disposal
CW	Cold Water	GFCI	Ground Fault Interrupter
COL	Column	GRND or GND	Ground
COM or CPRSR	Compressor	HACR	Heat-AC-Refrigeration
CONC B	Concrete Block	HGT, H or HT	Height
CND	Conduit	HOA	Hand-Off-Automatic
C.O. or -C.O.-	Conduit Only	HID	High Intensity Discharge
CONT	Contract	HOR	Horizontal
CU or COP	Copper	HB	Hose Bibb
CU FT.	Cubic Foot	HP	Horsepower
D	Diode or Rectifier	HTG	Heating
DC	Direct Current	HW	Hot Water
DET	Detail	HWH	Hot Water Heater
DIAG	Diagram	HZ	Hertz (cycles per second)
DIA	Diameter	I	Current
DIM	Dimension	" or IN	Inch
DISTR	Distribution	ID	Inside Diameter
DO	Door Opener	IMC	Intermediate Conduit
DT	Dust Tight or Double Throw	INT	Interior
DW	Dishwasher	JB	Junction Box
DWG	Drawing	K	One Thousand (1000)
D	Dryer	KCMIL	Thousand Circular Mils
EMT	Electrical Metallic Tubing	KIT	Kitchen

ABBREVIATIONS

KVA	Kilo Volt Amperes	PL	Pilot Light
KW	Kilo Watt	PNL	Panel
KWH	Kilo Watt Hour	PTN	Partition
L	Length or Lamps	PERP	Perpendicular
LTH	Lath	PL or PLAS	Plaster
LAU	Laundry	PLAT	Platform
LAV	Lavatory	PLBG	Plumbing
LG or LGTH	Length	P.O.C.	Point Of Connection
LOA	Length Overall	P	Porch
LOC	Location	PR	Pair
LEV	Level	PVC	Polyvinyl Chloride
LT	Light	PREFAB	Prefabricated
LTG	Lighting	PS	Pull Switch
LTS	Lights	RAD	Radiator
LM	lumens	R	Recessed, range or reset
L CL	Linen Closet	RECEPT or RCPT	Receptacle
LR	Living Room	RDM	Random
MAN	Manual	REC	Recessed
MN	Main	REF	Refrigerator
MATL	Material	REG	Registered
MAX	Maximum	REINF	Reinforce
M	Thousand (1000)	RPM	Revolutions per minute
MCC	Motor Control Center	REV	Reverse or Revision
MCM	Thousand Circular Mils	RF	Roof
MDP	Main Distribution Panel	RM or R	Room
MECH	Mechanical	RH	Range Hood
MIN	Minimum	RT	Raintight
MISC	Miscellaneous	SC	Scale
MOR	Middle Of Run	SCH	Schedule
MTR or MOT	Motor	S	Switch, Scuttle or South
MS	Motor Switch	SEL	Select
MT	Empty	SE or SERV	Service
MTD	Mounted	SEW	Sewer
N	North	SH	Sheet or Shower
NEU	Neutral	SK or S	Sink
NL	Night Light	SP	Spare
NO	Number	SPEC	Specifications
NTS	Not To Scale	SQ	Square
# or NO.	Number	SQ FT	Square Feet
O.C.B.	Oil Circuit Breaker	SQ IN	Square Inch
OC	Overcurrent	STD	Standard
O.C.	On Center	STL	Steel
OPNG	Opening	STK	Stock
OUT	Outlet	STG	Storage
OD	Outside Diameter	STR	Start
OA	Overall	SW or S	Switch
OUT	Outlet	T	Toilet
OVHD	Overhead	TEL	Telephone
PB	Push Button	THERMO	Thermostat
PC	Pull Chain	THK or T	Thick or Thickness
PF	Power Factor	TRANS or XFMR	Transformer

ABBREVIATIONS

TERM	Terminal
U.O.N.	Unless Otherwise Noted
U.O.S.	Under Other Specifications
UL	Underwriters Laboratory
UNEXC	Unexcavated
UNF	Unfinished
URM	Utility Room
V	Voltage or Vent
VA	Volt Amps
VD	Voltage Drop
VERT	Vertical
VT	Vapor Tight
WM	Washing Machine
W	Watt or Water
WC	Water Closet
WH	Water Heater
WP	Water Proof or Weatherproof
WT	Weight
W	West or Width
WTH	Width
XFMR	Transformer
Z	Reactance

OTHER BUILDING ABBREVIATIONS

AB	Anchor Bolt
ABV	Above
AC	Acoustical
ACFL	Access Floor
ACPL	Acoustical Plaster
ACT	Acoustical Tile
AD	Area Drain
ADD	Addendum
ADH	Adhesive
ADJ	Adjacent
AGG	Aggregate
ALT	Alternate
ANC	Anchor
ANOD	Anodized
AP	Access Panel
APX	Approximate
ARCH	Architect
ASB	Asbestos
ASPH	Asphalt
AUTO	Automatic
BBD	Bulletin Board
BD	Board
BEL	Below
BETW	Between
BIT	Bituminous
BLDG	Building
BLK	Block
BLKG	Blocking
BM	Bench Mark
BOT	Bottom
BPL	Bearing Plate
BRG	Bearing
BRK	Brick
BRZ	Bronze
BS	Both Sides
BSMT	Basement
BUR	Built-up Roof
BVL	Beveled
BW	Both Ways
CAB	Cabinet
CB	Catch Basin
CEM	Cement
CER	Ceramic
CFL	Counterflashing
CUFT	Cubic Foot
CG	Corner Guard
CHAM	Chamfer
CHBD	Chalkboard
CLGHT	Ceiling Height
CI	Cast Iron
CIR	Circle
CJ	Control Joint
CK	Caulk or Caulking
CLG	Ceiling
CLR	Clear or Clearance
CLS	Closure
CM	Centimeter
CMU	Concrete Masonry Unit
COL	Column
COMB	Combination
COMP	Compress
COMPT	Compartment
CONC	Concrete
CONST	Construction
CONT	Continuous
CONTR	Contract or Contractor
CORR	Corridor
CPR	Copper
CPT	Carpet
CRS	Course
CS	Countersink
CSMT	Casement

CT	Ceramic Tile	FCO	Floor Clean Out
CTR	Counter	FLG	Flashing
CUYD	Cubic Yard	FLR	Floor or Flooring
D	Drain	FLEX	Flexible
DEM	Demolish	FN	Fence
DEP	Depressed	FND	Foundation
DF	Drinking Fountain	FOC	Face Of Concrete
DH	Double Hung	FOF	Face Of Finish
DIAG	Diagonal	FOM	Face Of Masonry
DIAM	Diameter	FOS	Face Of Studs
DIM	Dimension	FP	Fireproof
DIV	Division	FPL	Fireplace
DL	Dead Load	FR	Frame or Framing
DMT	Demountable	FRC	Fire Retardant
DN	Down	FTG	Footing
DPR	Dampproofing	FUR	Furred or Furring
DR	Door	GA	Gauge
DRB	Drainboard	GB	Grab Bar
DS	Downspout	GC	General Contractor
DT	Drain Tile	GD	Grade
DET	Detail	GKT	Gasket
DTL	Detail	GL	Glass or Glazing
DW	Dumbwaiter	GLB	Glass Block
DWG	Drawing	GLF	Glass Fiber
E	East	GPDW	Gypsum Drywall
EB	Expansion Bolt	GRN	Granite
EJ	Expansion Joint	GST	Glazed Structural Tile
EL	Elevation	GT	Grout
ELEV	Elevator	GALV	Galvanized
EMER	Emergency	GVL	Gravel
ENC	Enclosure	HB	Hose Bibb
EQ	Equal	HBD	Hardboard
EQP	Equipment	HC	Hollow Core
ESC	Escalator	HDR	Header
EST	Estimate	HDW	Hardware
EWC	Electric Water Cooler	HM	Hollow Metal
EXCA	Excavate	HDRZ	Horizontal
EXIST	Existing	HP	High Point
EXH	Exhaust	HT	Height
EXP	Exposed	HTG	Heating
EXT	Exterior	HVAC	Heat, Ventilating & AC
ES	Each Side	HWD	Hardwood
FA	Fire Alarm	HWH	Hot Water Heater
FB	Face Brick	ID	Inside Diameter
FBD	Fiberboard	INCIN	Incinerator
FBO	Furnished By Others	INCL	Include
FBRK	Fire Brick	INS	Insulation
FD	Floor Drain	INT	Interior
FE	Fire Extinguisher	INTER	Intermediate
FEC	Fire Extinguisher Cabinet	INV	Invert
FF	Finished Floor	JC	Janitor's Closet
FBGL	Fiberglass	JF	Joint Filler
FHS	Fire Hose Station	JST	Joist
FIN	Finished	JT	Joint

KIT	Kitchen		O/O	Out To Out
KO	Knock Out		PAR	Parallel
KPL	Kick Plate		PB	Panic Bar
L	Length		PBD	Particle Board
LAB	Laboratory		PCC	Precast Concrete
LAD	Ladder		PCF	Pound Per Cubic Foot
LAM	Laminate		PE	Porcelain Enamel
LAV	Lavatory		PED	Pedestal
LB	Lag Bolt		PERF	Perforated
LBL	Label		PFL	Pounds Per Lineal Foot
LH	Left Hand		PREFIN	Prefinished
LL	Live Load		PK	Parking
LPT	Low Point		PLG	Plate Glass
LT	Light		PL	Property Line or Plate
LTL	Lintel		PLAM	Plastic Laminate
LVR	Louver		PLAS	Plaster
LW	Lightweight		PNL	Panel
M	Meter		PNT	Paint
MAS	Masonry		PSC	Prestressed Concrete
MAX	Maximum		PSF	Pounds Per Square Foot
MBR	Member		PSI	Pounds Per Square Inch
MC	Medicine Cabinet		PT	Point or Pressure Treat
MECH	Mechanical		PTC	Post Tensioned Concrete
MED	Medium		PTD	Paper Towel Receptor
MET	Metal		PVMT	Pavement
MFR	Manufacturer		PLYWD	Plywood
MH	Manhole		QT	Quarry Tile
MIN	Minimum		R	Riser
MIRR	Mirror		RA	Return Air
MISC	Miscellaneous		RAD	Radius
MLD	Moulding		RB	Rubber Base
MM	Millimeter		RBT	Rubber Tile
MEM	Membrane		RCP	Reinforced Concrete Pipe
MO	Masonry Opening		RD	Roof Drain
MOV	Movable		REINF	Reinforced
MR	Mop Receptor		REF	Reference or Refrigerator
MRB	Marble		REG	Register
MTFR	Metal Furring		REM	Remove
MAT	Material		RES	Resilient
MULL	Mullion		RET	Return
MWK	Millwork		REV	Revision
N	North		REFL	Reflective
NAT	Natural		RH	Right Hand
NIC	Not In Contract		S	South
NOM	Nominal		SC	Solid Core
NR	Noise Reduction		SCH	Schedule
NRC	Noise Reduction Coefficient		SCN	Screen
NTS	Not To Scale		SD	Storm Drain
OA	Overall		SEC	Section
OC	On Center		SFGL	Safety Glass
OD	Outside Diameter		SG	Sheet Glass
OH	Overhead		SHT	Sheet
OPG	Opening		SHTH	Sheathing
OPP	Opposite		SIM	Similar

SKL	Skylight	TZ	Terrazzo
SLT	Sealant	UC	Undercut
SP	Soundproof	UNF	Unfinished
SPEC	Specification	UNO	Unless Otherwise Noted
SPK	Speaker	UR	Urinal
SQ	Square	Var	Varnish or Variance
SK	Sink	VB	Vinyl Base
SST	Stainless Steel	VB	Vapor Barrier
STA	Station	VCI	Vinyl Composition Tile
STD	Standard	VERT	Vertical
STG	Seating	VF	Vinyl Fabric
STL	Steel	VIN	Vinyl
STO	Storage	VJ	V-Joint
STR	Structural	VNR	Veneer
SUS	Suspended	VT	Vinyl Tile
SYM	Symmetrical	VWC	Vinyl Wallcovering
SYN	Synthetic	W	West, Width or Wide
SYS	System	WB	Wood Base
T	Tread	WC	Water Closet or Wallcovering
TB	Towel Bar	WD	Wood
TEL	Telephone	WG	Wired Glass
T&G	Tongue & Groove	WH	Wall Hung
THK	Thick or Thickness	WI	Wrought Iron
THR	Threshold	WIN	Window
TKDB	Tackboard	WM	Wire Mesh
TOL	Tolerance	W/	With
TPD	Toilet Paper Dispenser	W/O	Without
TP	Toilet Partition	WP	Waterproofing
TR	Transom	WR	Water Repellent
TSL	Top Of Slab	WS	Water Stop
TST	Top Of Steel	WSCT	Wainscot
TV	Television	WTW	Wall To Wall
TYP	Typical	WWF	Welded Wire Fabric

FLOOR PLAN

This is a floor plan of a bedroom which indicates the location of the windows, doors, etc.

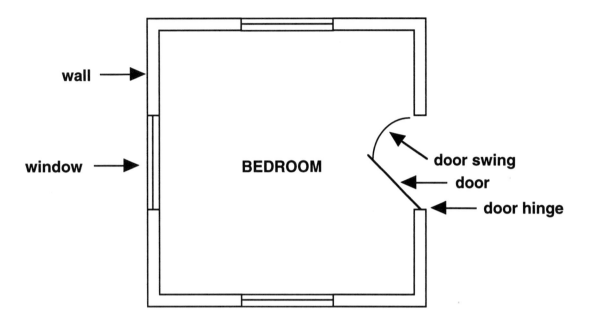

The floor plan is now showing the approximate location of the outlets and the types of outlets at each location. This floor plan shows a total of 6 outlets. Five for duplex receptacles and one television outlet.

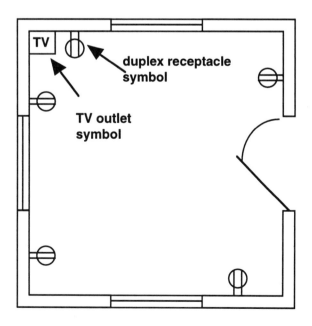

20

The floor plan now includes two more outlets. One indicating a ceiling light and the other outlet for a single-pole switch. The solid line from the light to the switch indicates the wiring is concealed in the ceiling. The line for the wiring has no slash marks, which represents a two-wire cable.

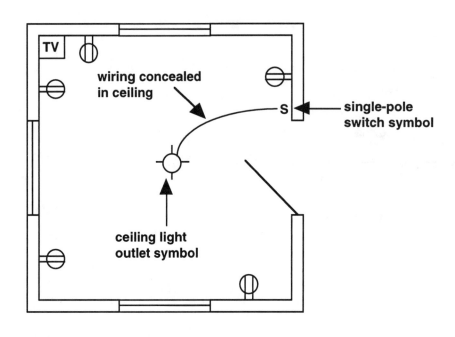

The floor plan now shows the source of supply to the bedroom from the lighting panel which is located in another part of the house.

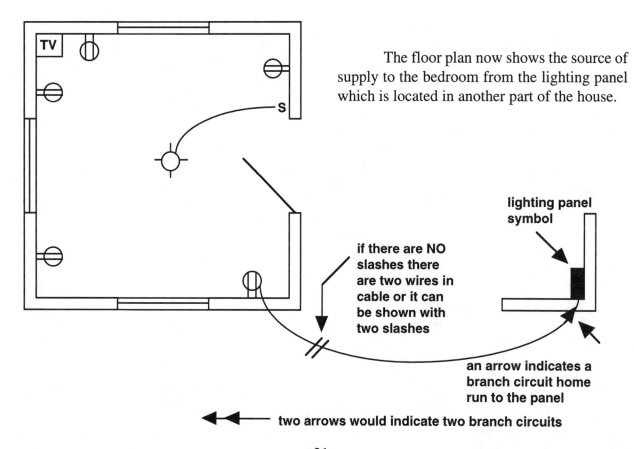

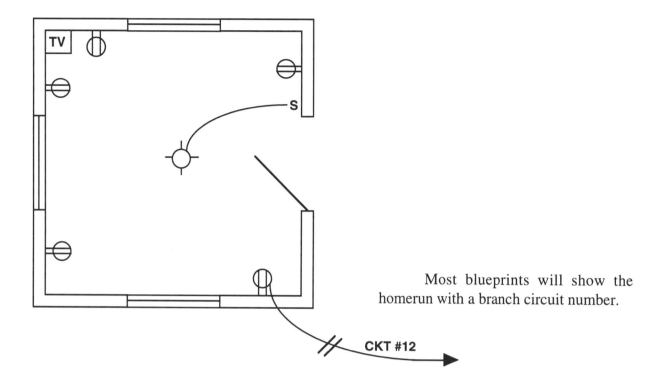

Most blueprints will show the homerun with a branch circuit number.

CKT #12

This branch circuit homerun indicates it will connect in the panelboard to circuit listed #12.

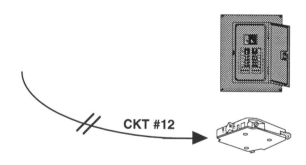

CKT #12

Later in this book it will explain panel schedules in detail. A panel schedule will list all the equipment, load, and the circuit it connects to.

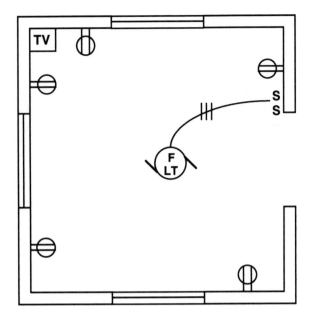

This floor plan shows a ceiling fan (paddle fan) with a light. Generally a double-gang box is installed with two single-pole switches. One switch is to control the fan motor and the other switch for the light. This would require a 3-wire cable from the double-gang box to the fan outlet box.

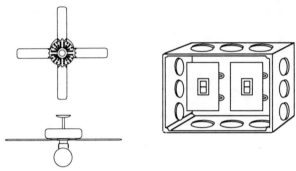

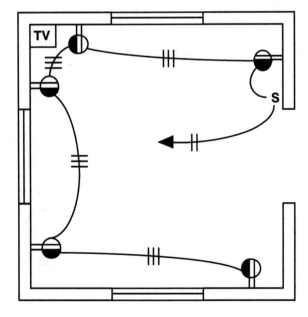

In some cases, instead of having a ceiling fixture, split-wired duplex receptacles are used.

By removing the tab on the hot side (brass colored) of the duplex you split it into two circuits. One half of the duplex will remain hot from the black wire and the other half will be energized from the red wire which is connected through the single-pole switch. This requires a 3-conductor cable between the receptacles as shown.

REMOVE TAB FOR SPLIT-WIRED DUPLEX RECEPTACLE

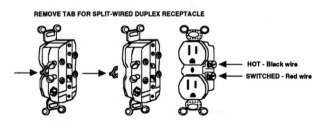

HOT - Black wire
SWITCHED - Red wire

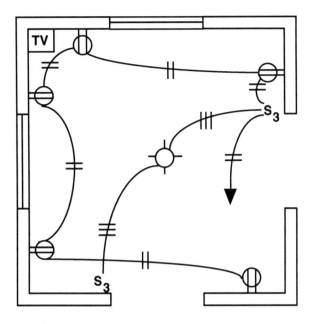

This room shows two door openings. A 3-way switch is installed at each opening so the ceiling light can be controlled at two locations.

The floor plan below has a sliding door to the outdoors. An outside light is wall mounted and has a single-pole switch. The ceiling light is controlled at both door openings by 3-way switches. An outdoor receptacle is required to be GFCI by the Code, the receptacle is of the weatherproof type.

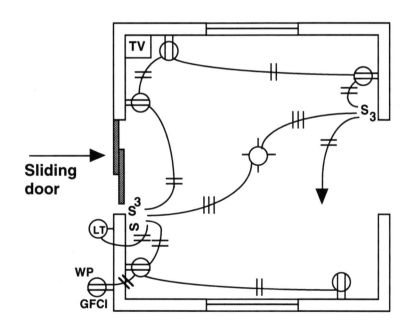

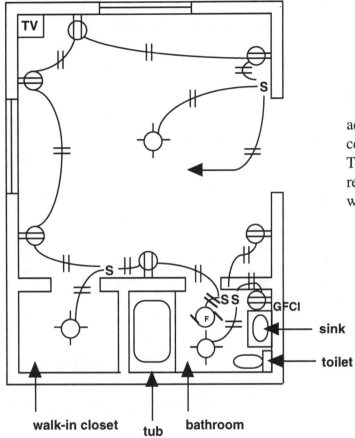

A walk-in closet and bathroom are added to the floor plan. Each room has a ceiling light controlled by a wall switch. The bathroom also has a required GFCI receptacle and a ceiling fan controlled by a wall switch.

walk-in closet   tub   bathroom

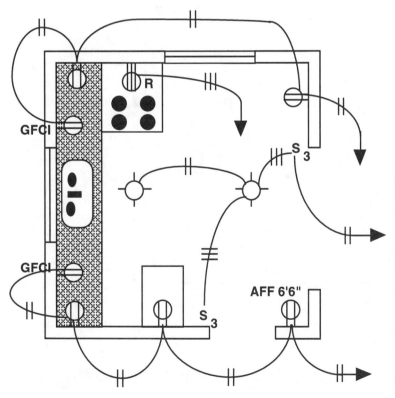

The kitchen shows a total of four branch circuits. The Code requires 2 - 20 amp small appliance circuits for the duplex receptacles. The receptacles within 6 feet of the sink are required to be GFCI. The lighting must be on a separate circuit. A special circuit is included for the range. A clock hanger receptacle is installed at 6' 6" above finish floor (AFF).

HOUSE PLAN H-6677

The floor plan shown is drawn to scale. 1/8" = 1'

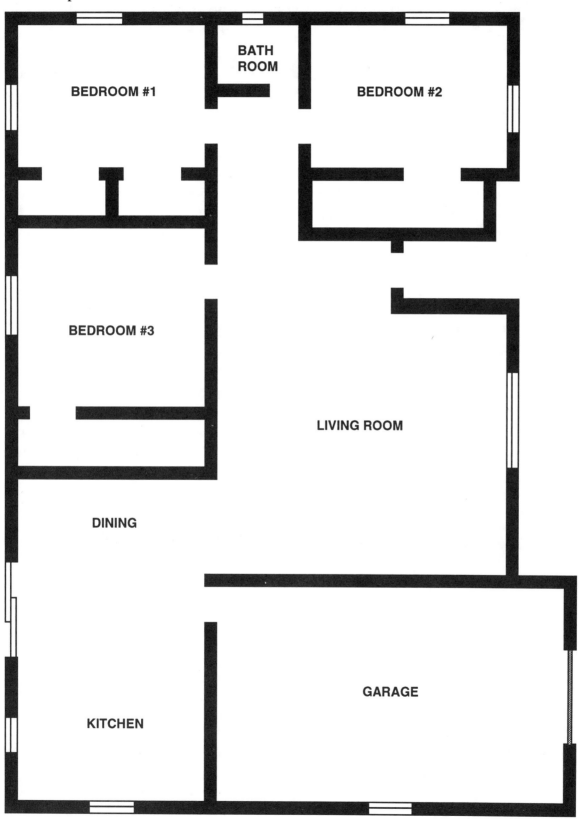

BATH ROOM

BEDROOM #1

BEDROOM #2

BEDROOM #3

LIVING ROOM

DINING

GARAGE

KITCHEN

Buildings are so large it would be impossible to draw a floor plan to size. A drawing is drawn to a reduced scale. This means all the distances are drawn smaller than the actual dimensions.

Example, if a floor plan is drawn to a scale of 1/4" = 1.0', each 1/4 inch on the drawing would equal one foot on the building. If the scale is 1/8" = 1.0', each 1/8 inch on the drawing would equal one foot on the building.

Some blueprints have several different drawings on the page, all with different scales.

Reading the scale on the blueprint is very important to the electrician. In some cases there are no measurements on the drawing, so the scale must be used to determine the correct location of outlets, boxes, equipment, etc.

Reading the scale wrong can be very expensive, as the location of the electrical outlets or stub-ups can be in the wrong location.

The Code reads in a dwelling unit (residence) receptacle outlets shall be installed so that no point along the floor line in any wall space is more than 6 feet, including any wall space 2 feet or more in width. The electrical designer laying out the floor plan will indicate the location of all outlets with the designated symbol. The blueprint will be designed with the Code rules upmost in their mind.

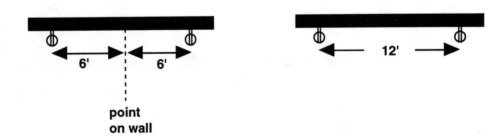

The Code spacing rules are the minimum requirements. In many cases extra outlets are added to the wall space to eliminate the use of extension cords. So the blueprint may show more outlets than the Code requires. The electrician is to make sure the Code minimum requirements are met when checking the blueprint to scale.

The view shown below is looking down on a bedroom. You can see, the 12 foot spacing on receptacles may require purchasing extensions cords after the furniture has been installed. Actually the best place to install a receptacle is behind the door, now close the door and you have an outlet you can plug into.

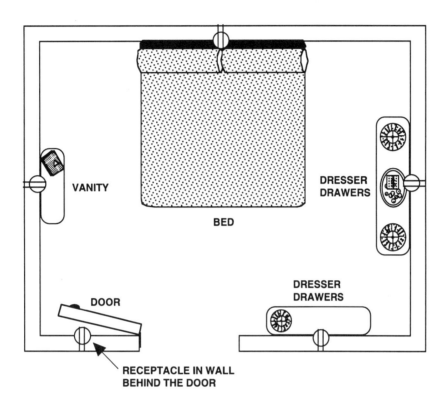

Scaled 1/8"= 1.0' bedroom #3
measures approximately 15' x 16'

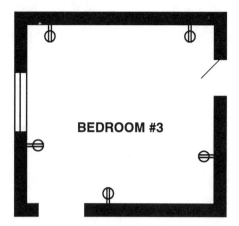

These five outlets will meet the
Code minimum requirements.

The kitchen-dining area measures approximately 16' x 27'. This is the most heavily loaded area of the house at 120 volts. The refrigerator, dishwasher, disposal, compactor, coffee pot, microwave oven, toaster, mixer, blender, etc. The Code requires a minimum of 2 - 20 amp small appliance 120v circuits, if it were my home I would install more than the Code minimum.

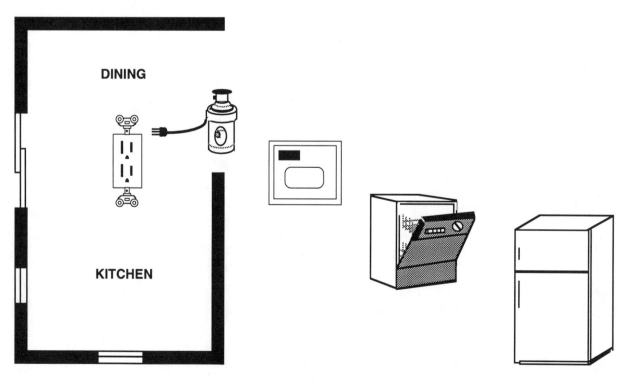

Some drawings include a symbol schedule as shown below. Not all electrical designers use the same symbols as they modify them to their desires. Always check the drawings for a symbol schedule.

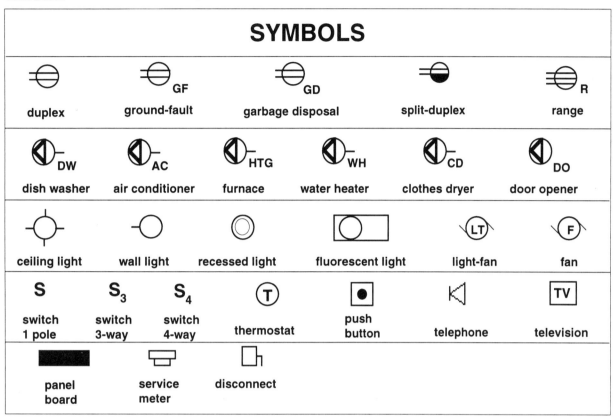

SYMBOLS

⊖ duplex	⊖ GF ground-fault	⊖ GD garbage disposal	⊖ split-duplex	⊖ R range
DW dish washer	AC air conditioner	HTG furnace	WH water heater	CD clothes dryer	DO door opener
ceiling light	wall light	recessed light	fluorescent light	LT light-fan	F fan
S switch 1 pole	S₃ switch 3-way	S₄ switch 4-way	T thermostat	● push button	◁ telephone	TV television
▬ panel board	service meter	disconnect		

A receptacle schedule is often found on electrical drawings where you have a variety of receptacle types.

RECEPTACLE TYPE SCHEDULE

Symbol	Amp rating	Wires-Poles	Voltage rating	NEMA type	Configuration	Remarks
⊖	20	3-W 2-P	125	5-20		duplex
⊖ R	50	3-W 3-P	125/ 250	10-50		range
⊘ CD	30	3-W 3-P	125/ 250	10-30		dryer

Now you can see the symbols being used in the floor plan to indicate the type of outlets. The range has a special 3-wire outlet, the receptacles within 6 feet of the sink are required to be ground-fault protected, the disposal has a separate receptacle, the dishwasher has a special outlet.

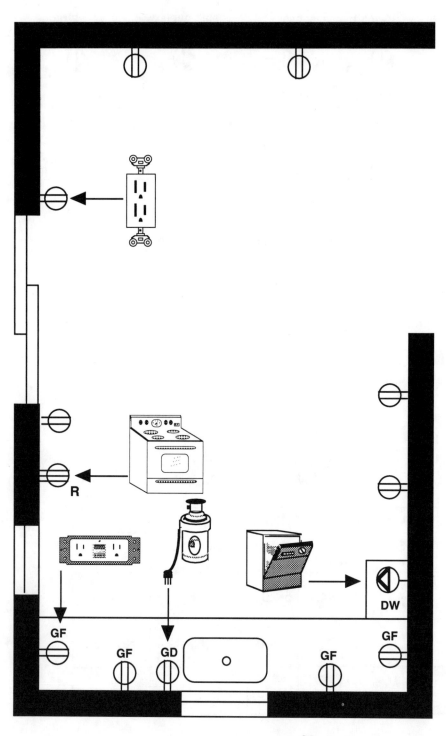

This floor plan show six circuits (homeruns). Three for the small appliance outlets, one for the dishwasher, one for the disposal and one for the range. The two slash marks indicate a two-wire circuit, the three slash marks on the range cable indicates a three-wire cable.

Often designers will omit the two slash marks from the drawing, after adding the switches and lighting outlets the drawing can become cluttered with several lines. To avoid confusion the cable with NO slash marks is a two-wire cable, any cable with MORE than two-wires will be noted with slash marks.

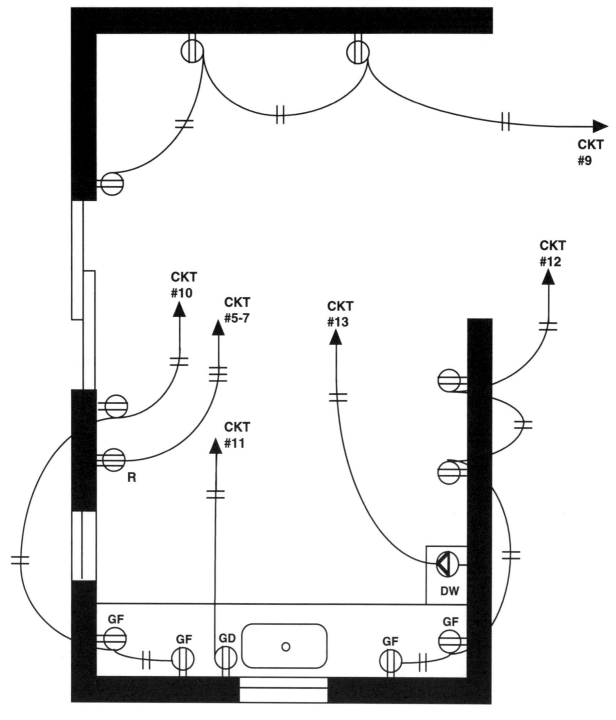

The kitchen lights are not allowed on the 20 amp small appliance circuits, so a separate circuit #10 is run for the lights.

The ceiling fan-light combo has two single-pole switches (one for fan and one for light) with a 3-wire cable to the fixture. The ceiling light is controlled from three locations by using two 3-way switches and one 4-way switch. The other lights are controlled by single-pole switches. •NO slash marks indicates 2-wire cable.

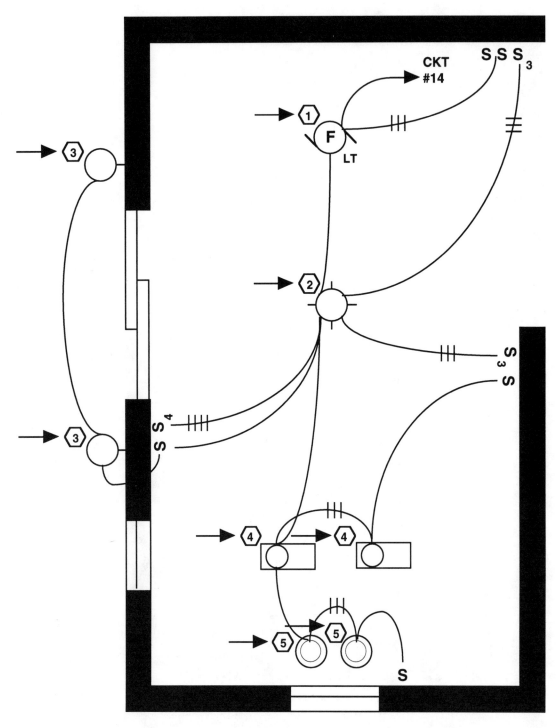

A lighting fixture schedule is a very helpful part of the electrical drawing. It shows the type by an indicator box. The fixture schedule lists the quantity, manufacturer and item number, type of mounting and even the lamp required for the fixture.

LIGHTING FIXTURE SCHEDULE				H - 6677	
Symbol	Type	Quantity	Manufacturer #	Mounting	Lamps
	1	1	Blowtime Inc. f-47338	surface	4-60w
	2	1	Brightlite Co. L-s 23975	surface	100w
	3	2	Outdoor Lumens R-72w	wall	60w
	4	2	Quicklite Inc. F-5649	surface	2-40w WW
	5	2	Intense Lighting R-1275	recessed	60w

Shown below is the ceiling light which is controlled from three locations, which requires four wires from the 4-way switch to the ceiling outlet box, three wires from each 3-way switch to the ceiling outlet box, and a 2-wire cable which is the 120 volt source wire.

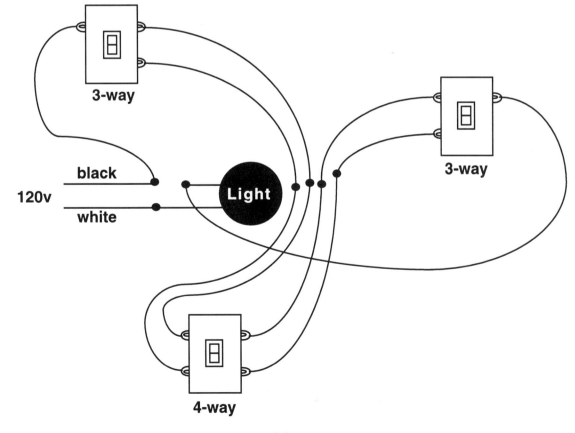

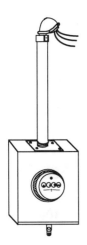

The location of the service to a building is extremely important as this is where the big money is spent.

The service can be overhead or underground. The key in a residence is to locate the service and panelboard close to the heaviest loads. The heaviest loads would be the highest wattage appliances such as the range, water heater, clothes dryer, air conditioner, electric heat, etc.

These appliances require the larger size cable which is the money factor. Always try to keep these circuits at a minimum distance from the panelboard.

A garage that is close to the kitchen is an excellent location for the panelboard.

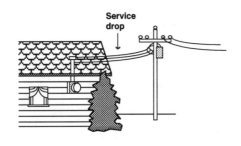

Service drop

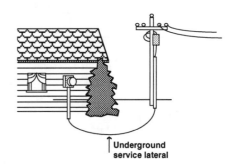

Underground service lateral

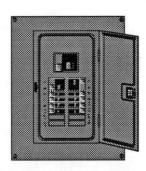

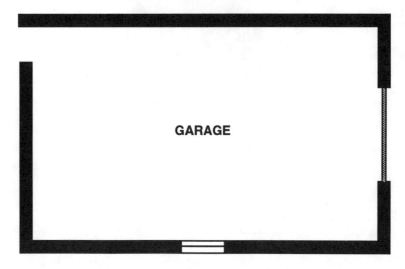

GARAGE

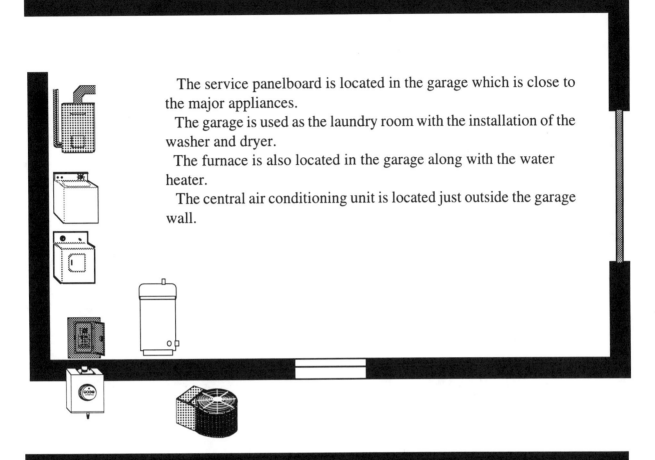

The service panelboard is located in the garage which is close to the major appliances.

The garage is used as the laundry room with the installation of the washer and dryer.

The furnace is also located in the garage along with the water heater.

The central air conditioning unit is located just outside the garage wall.

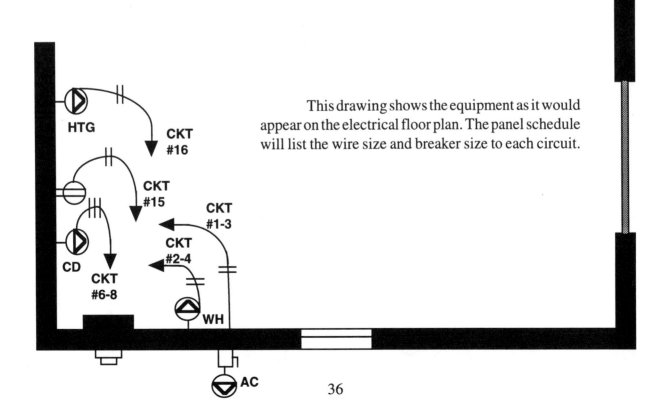

HTG

CKT #16

CKT #15

CKT #1-3

CKT #2-4

CD

CKT #6-8

WH

AC

This drawing shows the equipment as it would appear on the electrical floor plan. The panel schedule will list the wire size and breaker size to each circuit.

This drawing shows the remaining outlets in the garage. Circuit #17 is a required GFCI circuit to the receptacles. Circuit #18 is feeding the lights and overhead door opener.

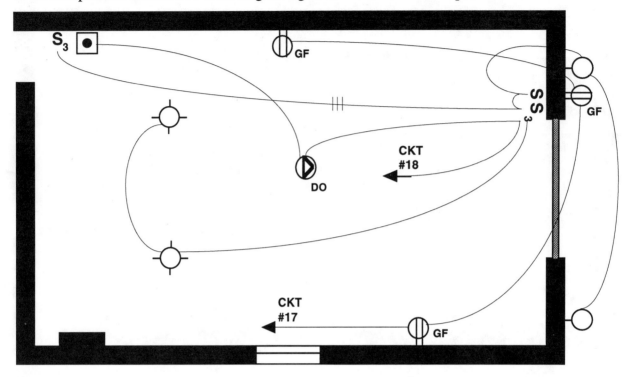

Circuit #19 feeds the living room which is an area of the house that is lightly loaded. Two 3-ways and one 4-way switch is used to control the split-receptacles which are used in place of ceiling lights. Special wiring is required for the cable TV, telephones and thermostat.

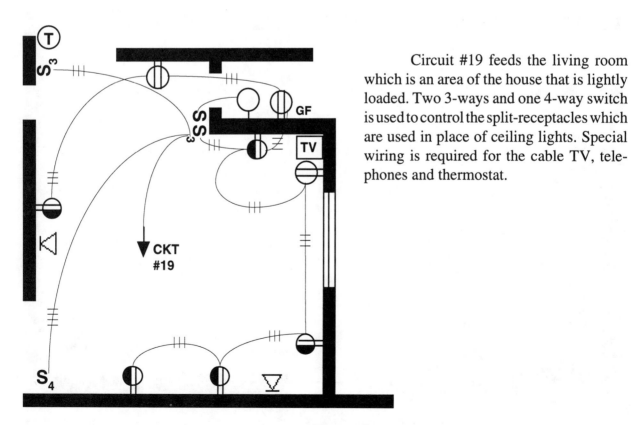

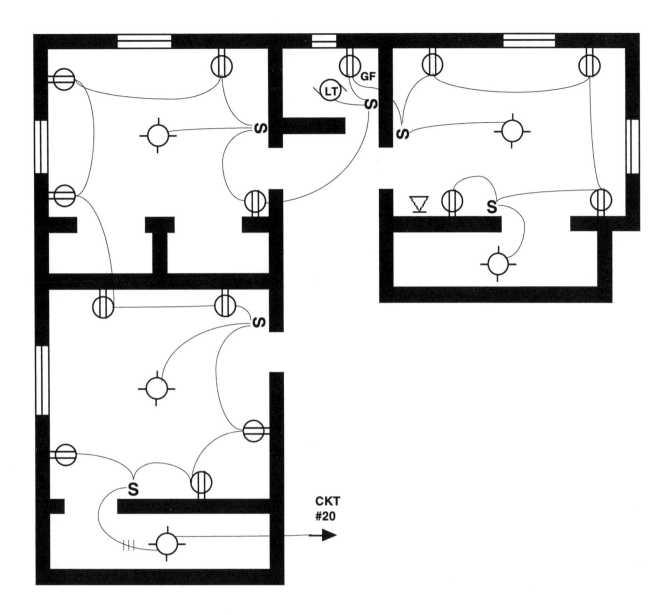

Circuit #20 is feeding the receptacles and lighting to the bedrooms. This area of the house contains very light loading.

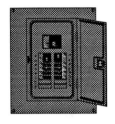

Shown below is one type of a panelboard schedule. There are many different versions. We will illustrate other schedules throughout this book.

A schedule is a very handy working tool for the electrician as an electrical item can be fully described using a minimum of text. This allows the electrician to see a clear picture of the circuit components.

The electrical drawings may contain several schedules. A lighting fixture schedule, connected-load (for balancing) schedule, electric-heat schedule, kitchen-equipment schedule, receptacle-type schedule, etc.

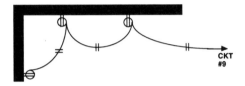

Example: This panelboard circuit shows that **CKT #9** connects to **CIRCUIT 9** in the panelboard, it is a single-pole 20 amp circuit breaker, using a #12-2 conductor, and it serves the dining room.

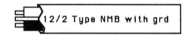

PANELBOARD SCHEDULE				H - 6677	
MAINS 150 **PHASE** 1		**VOLTS** 240/120		**AMPERE** 150	
Circuit Number	Circuit Breaker		Conductor		Serves
	Poles	Amps	Number of	Size	
1	2	35	2	#8	Air Conditioner
2	2	30	2	#10	Water Heater
3	▬	▬	▬	▬	Air Conditioner
4	▬	▬	▬	▬	Water Heater
5	2	50	3	#6	Range
6	2	30	3	#10	Dryer
7	▬	▬	▬	▬	Range
8	▬	▬	▬	▬	Dryer
9	1	20	2	#12	Dining Room
10	1	20	2	#12	Kitchen - SW
11	1	20	2	#12	Garbage Disposal
12	1	20	2	#12	Kitchen - SE
13	1	20	2	#12	Dishwasher
14	1	20	2	#12	Kitchen Lights-Fan
15	1	20	2	#12	Washer
16	1	20	2	#12	Furnace
17	1	20	2	#12	Garage Recpts.
18	1	20	2	#12	Garage Lights, etc
19	1	20	2	#12	Living Room
20	1	20	2	#12	Bedrooms-Bath

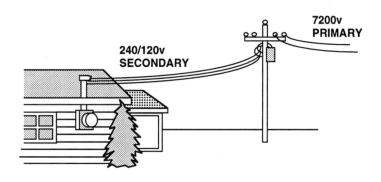

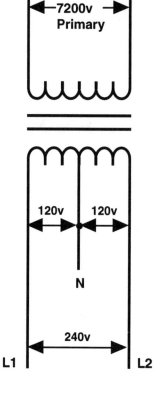

To fully understand a panelboard schedule it is necessary to understand how the panelboard is fed and the voltage relationships.

This is a single-phase 3-wire 240/120v secondary feeding the panelboard with L1 (line one), L2 (line two) and N (neutral).

The voltage between L1 and L2 is 240 volts. The voltage from either L1 or L2 to the neutral is 120 volts.

The main circuit breaker installed in the panelboard receives the 240 volts from the service conductors and feeds the voltage to the L1 and L2 busbars.

The main breaker provides overcurrent protection for the panelboard and it is also used as a disconnecting means to shut power off to the panelboard.

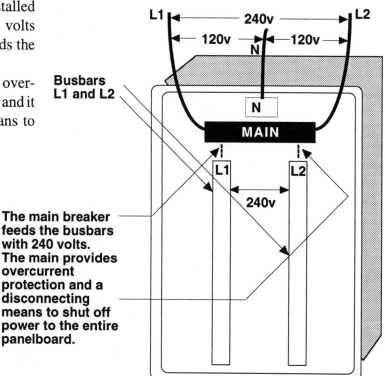

Busbars L1 and L2

The main breaker feeds the busbars with 240 volts. The main provides overcurrent protection and a disconnecting means to shut off power to the entire panelboard.

40

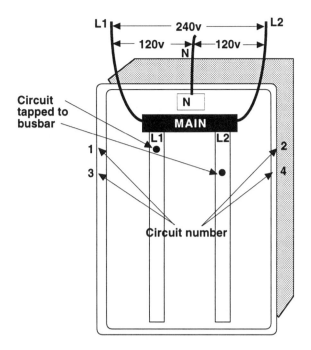

The circuits are numbered with odd numbers on the left and even numbers on the right. For the circuit to receive voltage it must have a tapped connection to the busbar.

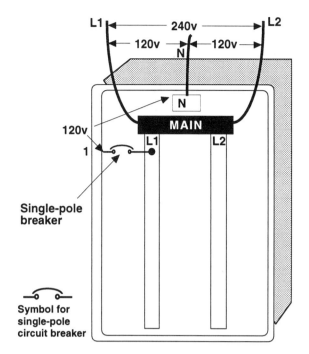

For circuit #1 to receive 120 volts the breaker is connected to L1. The 120 volts is received from L1 to N.

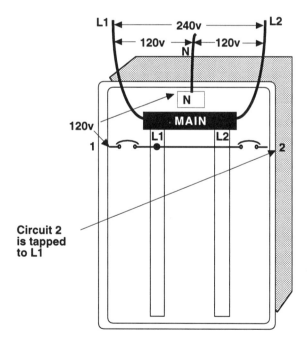

For circuit #2 to receive 120 volts the breaker is connected to L1. The 120 volts is received from L1 to N.

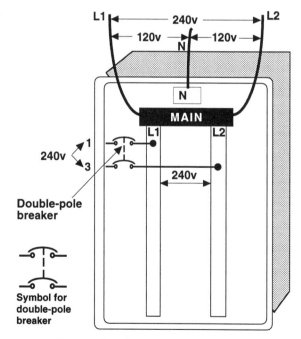

For a circuit to receive the higher 240 volts it must be connected to both L1 and L2 using a double-pole breaker. Circuits 1 and 3 are tapped to L1 and L2.

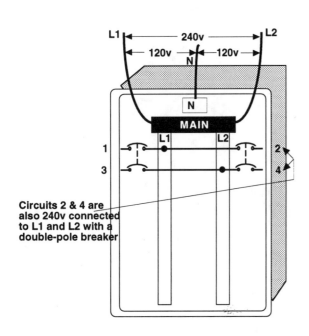

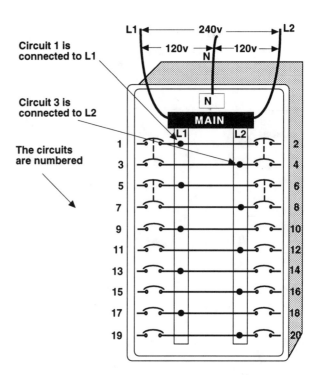

Circuit 2 is tapped to L1 and circuit 4 is tapped to L2. By installing a double-pole breaker 240 volts is supplied to the circuit.

Circuits 1 & 3, 2 & 4, 5 & 7, 6 & 8 are 240 volt double-pole breakers. Circuits 9, 10, 11, 12, 13, 14, 15, 16, 17, 18, 19, and 20 are 120 volts with single-pole breakers.

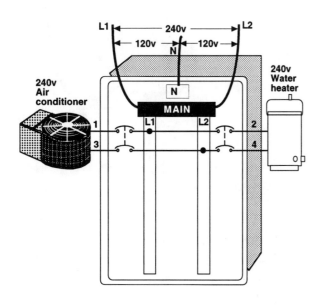

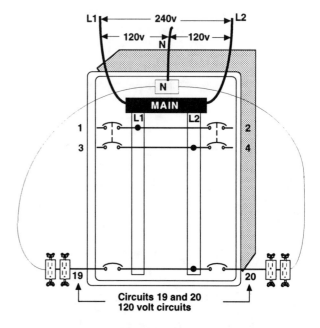

Circuits 1 and 3 are feeding the 240v A/C unit. Circuits 2 and 4 are feeding the 240v water heater.

Circuits 19 and 20 are feeding 120 volt receptacle circuits.

The actual connected loads are shown in the load balancing schedule. It is very important that the electrician connect the circuits as shown in the panelboard schedule to maintain the best possible balance.

LOAD BALANCE SCHEDULE				H - 6677
Description	Load	L1	L2	N
Air conditioner	6720	3360	3360	
Water heater	5000	2500	2500	
Range	12000	6000	6000	•8400
Dryer	5000	2500	2500	5000
Dining room	2400	2400		2400
Kitchen-SW	2400		2400	2400
Disposal	1176	1176		1176
Kitchen-SE	2400		2400	2400
Dishwasher	1200	1200		1200
Kitchen Lts-fan	1356		1356	1356
Washer	1176	1176		1176
Furnace	1176		1176	1176
Garage Recpts.	2400	2400		2400
Garage Lts.-Etc.	2400		2400	2400
Living room	2400	2400		2400
Bedroom-Bath	2400		2400	2400
TOTAL	51604	25112	26492	36384

PANELBOARD SCHEDULE					H- 6677	
MAINS 150	PHASE 1		VOLTS 240/120		AMPERE 150	
Circuit Number	Circuit Breaker		Conductor		Serves	
	Poles	Amps	Number of	Size		
1	2	35	2	#8	Air Conditioner	
2	2	30	2	#10	Water Heater	
3	▬	▬	▬	▬	Air Conditioner	
4	▬	▬	▬	▬	Water Heater	
5	2	50	3	#6	Range	
6	2	30	3	#10	Dryer	
7	▬	▬	▬	▬	Range	
8	▬	▬	▬	▬	Dryer	
9	1	20	2	#12	Dining Room	
10	1	20	2	#12	Kitchen - SW	
11	1	20	2	#12	Garbage Disposal	
12	1	20	2	#12	Kitchen - SE	
13	1	20	2	#12	Dishwasher	
14	1	20	2	#12	Kitchen Lights-Fan	
15	1	20	2	#12	Washer	
16	1	20	2	#12	Furnace	
17	1	20	2	#12	Garage Recpts.	
18	1	20	2	#12	Garage Lights, etc	
19	1	20	2	#12	Living Room	
20	1	20	2	#12	Bedrooms-Bath	

AIR CONDITIONER

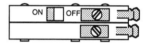

35 amps = 8400 va

The air conditioner has a connected load of 6720va. The 35 amp circuit would actually provide 35a x 240v = 8400va.

The 20 amp, 120 volt branch circuits throughout the house that are feeding receptacles have unknown loads, as it cannot be predetermined exactly what will be plugged into the receptacles, so a connected load is not known. The 20a x 120v will provide 2400 va per circuit fully loaded.

20 amp branch circuit 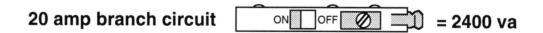 **= 2400 va**

Circuit #14 feeding the kitchens lights and fan are known loads as they are hard-wired and are not plug and cord connected to receptacles. The light fixture schedule shows the lights add up to a total of 660 watts and the fan is a 1/4 hp (5.8a x 120v = 696va) for a total connected load of 1356 on circuit #14. The 20 amp circuit will provide 2400va.

All loads will connect to a line wire, but not all loads connect to the neutral, this is why the neutral can generally be reduced in size.

The air conditioner and water heater have no neutral connection so there is no neutral load. The range and dryer have a neutral and the Code requires a 70% of the load to be on the neutral. The washer, disposal, dishwasher are 120 volt loads.

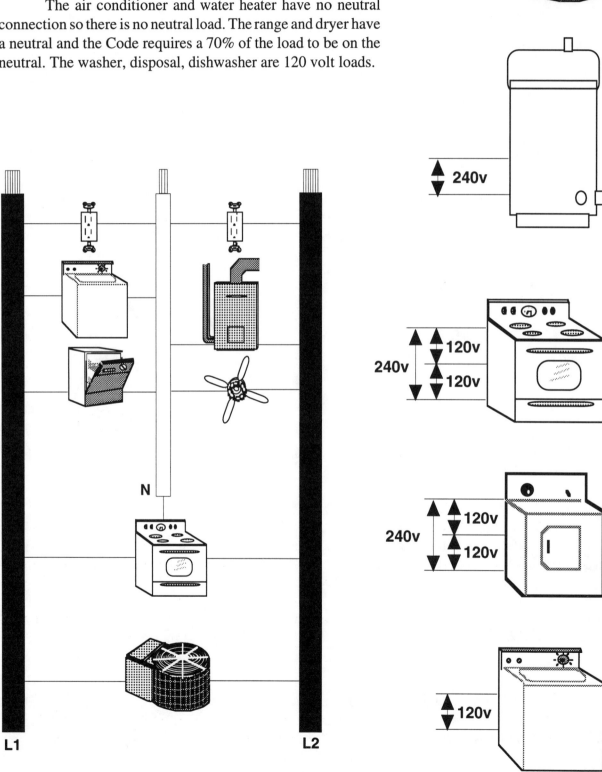

240v

240v

240v / 120v / 120v

240v / 120v / 120v

120v

N

L1   L2

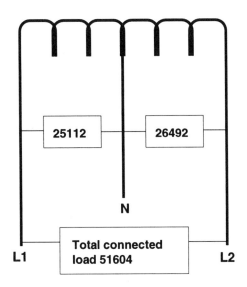

The total connected load is 51,604va/240v = 215 amps.

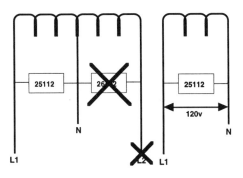

If Line 2 was completely shut off Line 1 would carry 25112va/120v = 209 amps.

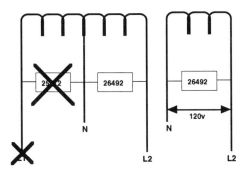

If Line 1 was completely shut off Line 2 would carry 26492va/120v = 221 amps.

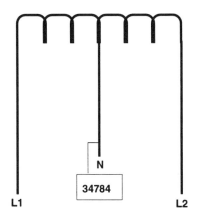

The neutral shows a connected load of 36284/240v = 151 amps. The •8400 @ 70% makes no logic, but the Code requires 70%. Most ranges only have a time clock and light that are connected to the 120v neutral, hardly a 8400/240 = 35 amp load. The worst condition on the neutral would only be 50% (the maximum unbalance) of 12kw = 6000.

There is no 70% on the neutral for a dryer **branch circuit**. If the dryer had a 1/2 hp, 120v drive motor the amperage is 9.8, plus a time clock and a light. 5000/240v = 21 amps would cover the neutral for the dryer branch circuit.

Example: The 12kw range has four cook-top elements which are 240 volts connected with low-medium-high settings. The range has an oven with 240 volt connected elements. The range has a 120 volt connected clock and light.

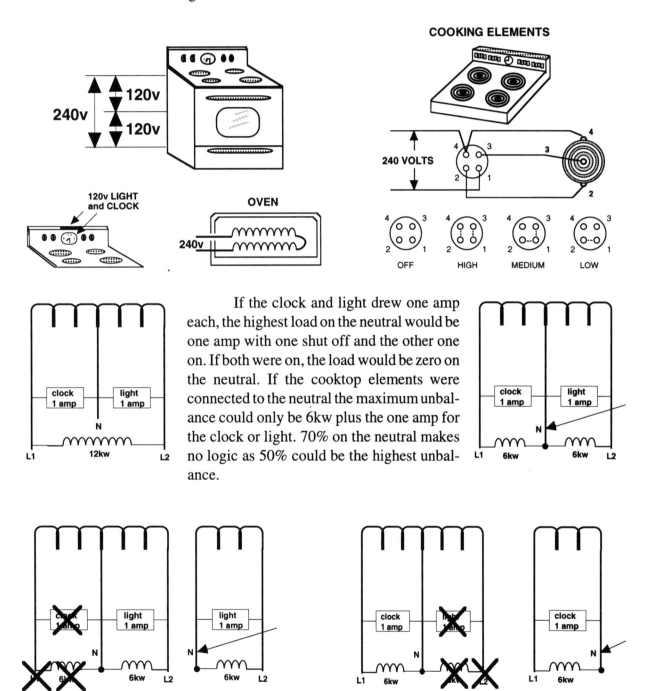

If the clock and light drew one amp each, the highest load on the neutral would be one amp with one shut off and the other one on. If both were on, the load would be zero on the neutral. If the cooktop elements were connected to the neutral the maximum unbalance could only be 6kw plus the one amp for the clock or light. 70% on the neutral makes no logic as 50% could be the highest unbalance.

THE NEUTRAL CARRIES THE UNBALANCED CURRENT

Example: The dryer has a 1/2 hp, 120v motor to turn the drum, timer and maybe a 120v control light. The heating element is 240v connected.

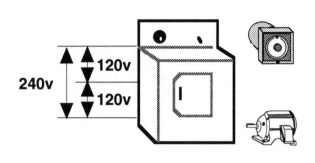

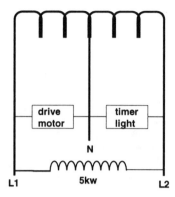

It is important for the electrician reading the drawings to have a mental picture of how the loads are connected and balanced.

The reason for balancing loads on the neutral is to ensure that the neutral conductor never has to carry a large amount of current. If the loads are unbalanced, considerable current will flow in the neutral conductor. The neutral conductor is sized by the designer by balancing loads, if the loads are **not** connected as shown on the drawing schedule, overheating can occur causing insulation damage to the neutral conductor.

Shown below is how the AC sine wave looks on a 240 volt secondary winding.

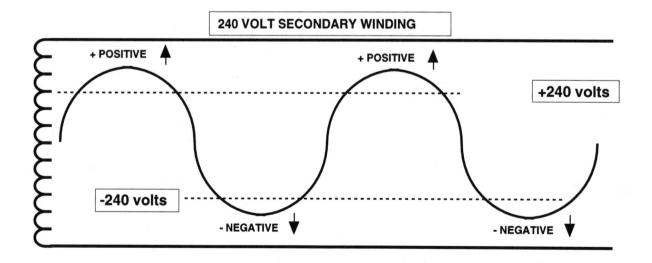

Shown below is the voltage relationship between L1 - L2 and the neutral. When the upper half of the winding (L1-N) is in the positive alternation, the lower half of the winding (L2-N) is in the negative alternation. These two sine waves (positive and negative) are said to be 180° out of phase with each other. When L1 is positive, L2 is negative.

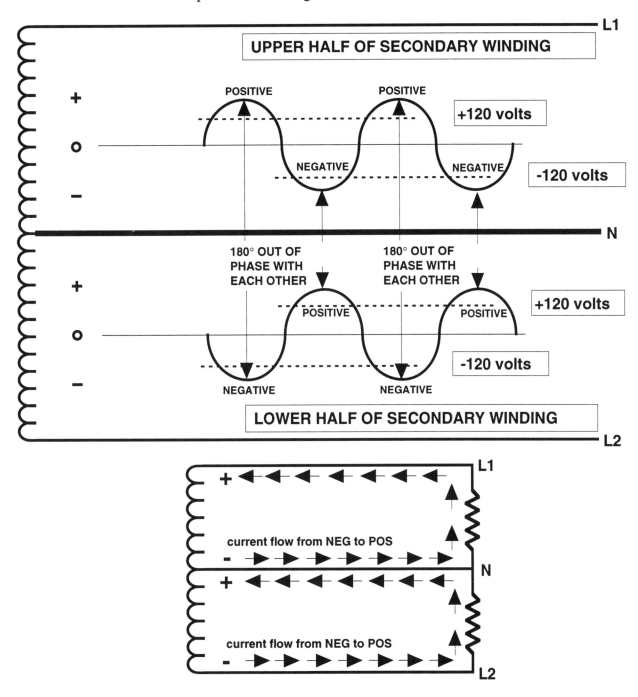

As you can see, current flow in the upper half of the winding (L1-N) is in one direction through the neutral conductor. In the lower winding (L2-N), the current flow is in the opposite direction through the neutral conductor. If the loads are the same the neutral would carry zero current as the upper circuit current (L1-N) cancels the lower circuit current (L2-N) in the neutral conductor.

BALANCED LOADS

With both loads balanced at 20 amps each, the upper winding current of 20 amps is flowing in one direction in the neutral conductor while at the same time the lower winding current of 20 amps is flowing in the opposite direction in the neutral conductor. The currents cancel each other, so the neutral conductor is carrying zero current.

In fact, if the loads were **always** equal, you could remove the neutral conductor. Of course, this is never the case.

UNBALANCED LOADS

With an unbalanced condition as shown with one 20 amp load and one 10 amp load the neutral would carry the unbalance of 10 amps.

From L1 to N the neutral conductor has 20 amps flowing in one direction, from L2 to N the neutral conductor has 10 amps flowing in the opposite direction. The 10 amps from L2-N will cancel 10 of the 20 amps from L1-N, thus leaving the unbalance of 10 amps flowing in the neutral conductor.

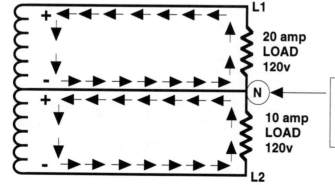

NEUTRAL CARRIES THE UNBALANCED LOAD 10 AMPS

Determining the minimum size service is accomplished by a step-by-step procedure. The designer, inspector, plans examiner, electrician, etc. are responsible for the installation of the service to be within the requirements of the Code.

Since not all the connected loads will be turned on and fully loaded at the same time, the Code permits reducing the size of the connected load when determining the size of the service.

House plan **H -6677**

Example: A dwelling has a total of 2394 sq.ft. of living area (outside dimensions) with the following equipment:

5 hp air conditioner 28a x 240v	=	6720
5 kw water heater	=	5000
12 kw range	=	12000
5 kw dryer	=	5000
1/2 hp disposal 9.8a x 120v	=	1176
1200 va dishwasher	=	1200
1/4 hp kitchen fan 5.8 x 120v	=	696
1/2 hp furnace blower motor	=	1176
1/4 hp garage door opener	=	696

The Code requires a minimum of 3va per square foot of living area be calculated. This load is for the 120v receptacles throughout the house (with the exception of the small appliance and laundry receptacles).

The Code requires a minimum of 1500va each for a minimum of two small appliance circuits. This minimum calculated load is for all the 120v receptacles in the kitchen and dining room. This is the heaviest loaded area of the house, 120 volts.

The Code requires a minimum of 1500va be calculated into the size of the service conductor for the laundry. This is the 120 volt receptacle for the washing machine.

The Code permits a demand (reduction) to be applied to this calculated receptacle load. The first 3000va cannot be reduced, but the next 117,000va can be reduced 35%.

	LINE LOAD	NEUTRAL LOAD
2394 sq.ft. x 3va	= 7182va	7182va
Small appliance 2 x 1500va	= 3000va	3000va
Laundry	= 1500va	1500va
Total 120v receptacle load	= 11682va	11682va

(First three rows and totals crossed out)

The 11682va can be reduced:		
1st 3000va @ 100%	= 3000va	3000va
Next 8682va @ 35%	= 3039va	3039va
Total 120v receptacle demand load	**= 6039va**	**6039va**

The 11682va is now reduced to 6039va.

	LINE LOAD	NEUTRAL LOAD
The air conditioner load is 6720 with no neutral.	= 6720	0
The 5kw water heater is a fastened in place appliance and has a 75% demand. There is no neutral.	= 3750	0
The 12kw range is permitted a demand of 8kw with 70% on the neutral.	= 8000	5600
The 5kw dryer requires 70% on the neutral.	= 5000	3500
The 1/2 hp (9.8a x 120v) disposal is a fastened in place appliance and has a 75% demand.	= 882	882
The 1200va dishwasher is a fastened in place appliance and has a 75% demand.	= 900	900
The 1/4 hp (5.8a x 120v) kitchen fan is a fastened in place appliance and has a 75% demand.	= 522	522
The 1/2 hp (9.8a x 120v) furnace blower motor is a fastened in place appliance @ 75%.	= 882	882
The 1/4 hp (5.8a x 120v) door opener is a fastened in place appliance @ 75%.	= 522	522
The Code requires that 25% of the largest motor be added to the service demand. The A/C is the largest motor at 6720 x 25%.	= 1680	0

TOTAL LINE DEMAND **= 34,897** NEUTRAL = **18,847**

LINE CONDUCTOR SIZE

34,897/240v = 145 amps

NEUTRAL CONDUCTOR SIZE

18,847/240v = 79 amps

The selection of a panelboard is first determined by the number of circuits it must supply. Then the panelboard size is determined by the **calculated** load it will supply. The calculated load is 145 amperes minimum. The next higher standard size service is 150 amps.

A panelboard may have a busbar current rating **larger** than the calculated load, but never less than the calculated load.

The overcurrent protection (main) cannot be larger than the **rating** of the panelboard.

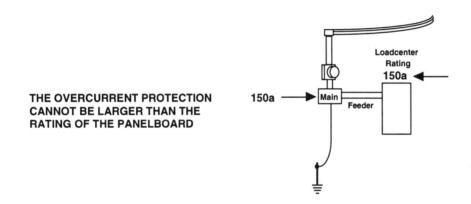

THE OVERCURRENT PROTECTION CANNOT BE LARGER THAN THE RATING OF THE PANELBOARD

Often the question arises, can you install 150 amp service cable to a 200 amp, 30 circuit main lug panel, with a 150 amp main breaker? The answer is YES!

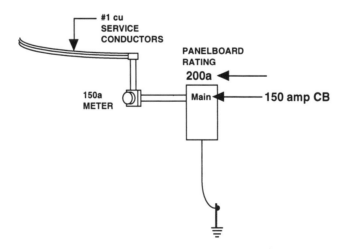

Sometimes you find there is a need for a panelboard with a main breaker that has a current rating LESS than the normally required rating of the panelboard to have the number of branch circuits required.

The Code states each lighting and appliance panelboard shall be individually protected on the supply side by not more than two main circuit breakers or two sets of fuses having a combined rating not greater than that of the panelboard. The exception to this rule is, individual protection for a lighting and appliance panelboard shall **not** be required if the panelboard **feeder** has overcurrent protection not greater than the rating of the panelboard.

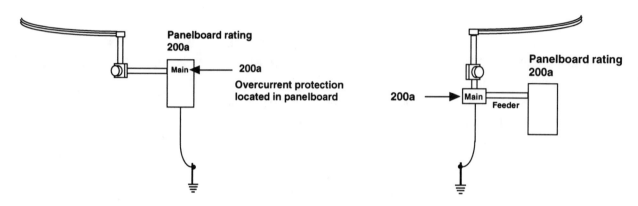

A panelboard might be a service equipment panelboard, distribution panelboard, or a branch-circuit panelboard. A single panelboard could combine two of these functions, or all three within a single cabinet.

If the panelboard is used as a service equipment panelboard, it must be marked **suitable for service equipment**.

The most common panelboard is the lighting and appliance panelboard. No more than 42 overcurrent devices (in addition to the main) may be installed.

It is very important to understand the definition of a **lighting and appliance** branch circuit panelboard.

The Code defines a lighting and appliance panelboard as one having **more** than 10% of its overcurrent devices rated **30 amps or less**, for which **neutral connections** are provided.

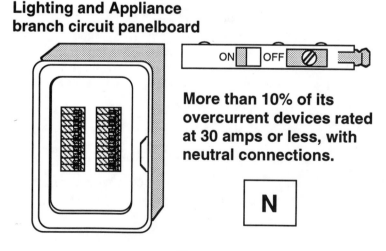

Lighting and Appliance branch circuit panelboard

More than 10% of its overcurrent devices rated at 30 amps or less, with neutral connections.

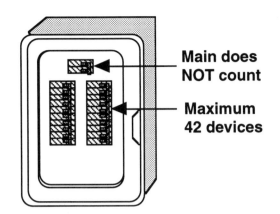

Main does NOT count

Maximum 42 devices

The lighting and appliance panelboard can contain up to 42 overcurrent devices maximum. The main overcurrent device is NOT counted.

MAIN

1-POLE COUNTS 1

2-POLE COUNTS 2

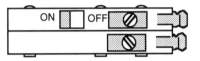

3-POLE COUNTS 3

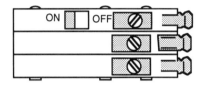

Different manufacturers of panelboards make different sizes of ampere ratings and spaces for single-phase and three-phase panelboards.

Manufacturer "X"		Manufacturer "Y"	
SINGLE-PHASE		**SINGLE-PHASE**	
Ampere Rating	Spaces	Ampere Rating	Spaces
60a	12-18-24	100a	12-20
100a	12-18-24	125a	30-42
150a	30-36-42	150a	30-42
225a	12-18-24-30-36-42	175a	30-42
		200a	30-42
		225a	30-42

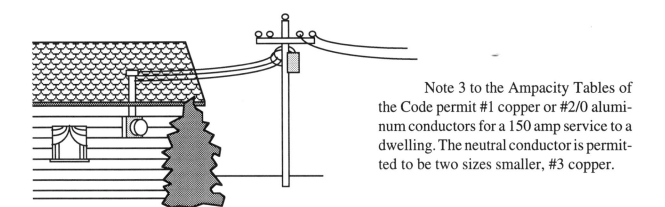

Note 3 to the Ampacity Tables of the Code permit #1 copper or #2/0 aluminum conductors for a 150 amp service to a dwelling. The neutral conductor is permitted to be two sizes smaller, #3 copper.

GROUNDING

The required grounding electrode conductor is a #6 copper sized from Code Table 250-94 of the largest service-entrance conductor which is a #1 copper.

System grounding means that the service neutral conductor, grounding electrode conductor, service entrance equipment, and all metallic pipes, must be **bonded** together at the **service**. The equipment grounding conductor or raceway is bonded to the neutral and grounding electrode conductor at the neutral block in the **service equipment panel only.**

The number one **violation** of grounding is the bonding of the grounded neutral at sub-panels and other locations throughout the electrical system.

The main bonding jumper in the service equipment panel may be a wire, bus, screw or similar connector. Generally, installing the **bonding screw** through the neutral block to the service panel is the most common main bonding jumper used.

Bonding Screw

The sketch below shows the neutral bus in the service panel properly **bonded** to the panel and electrode. The service equipment enclosure is called the "bullseye" of grounding. The service equipment is the **only** location where all the grounding is connected together.

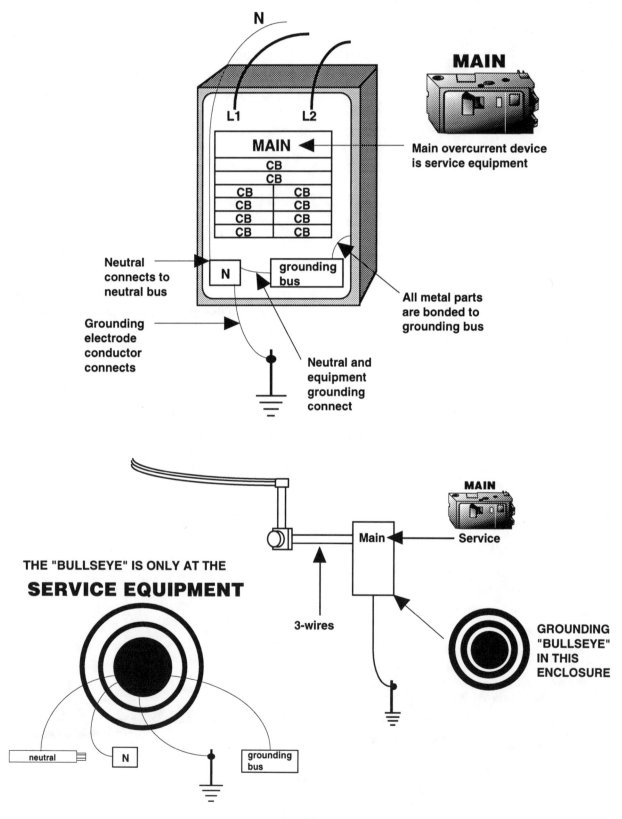

Some areas have a local Code which requires the main disconnect to be on the outside of a building. In case of a fire, the fireman can disconnect the electrical service without going into the building.

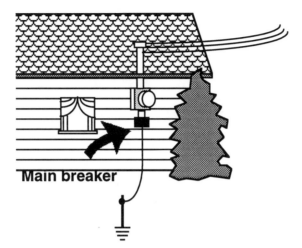

Main breaker

With the main breaker outside of the house, the wiring between the main breaker and the panelboard inside of the house is called a **feeder**. This requires 4-wires; two ungrounded hot wires, one neutral, and one equipment grounding conductor.

The neutral conductor, equipment grounding conductor, and grounding electrode conductor would all be bonded together in the main breaker panel on the **outside** of the house. The panelboard inside the house would have the neutral and equipment grounding conductor **isolated** from each other. The neutral would **not** be bonded to the panelboard. **Only at the service equipment is the neutral bus bonded to the metal cabinet**.

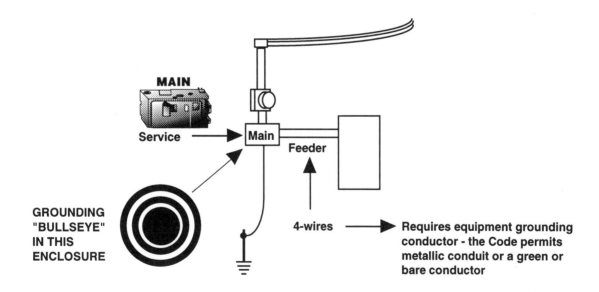

MAIN

Service → Main

Feeder

GROUNDING
"BULLSEYE"
IN THIS
ENCLOSURE

4-wires → Requires equipment grounding conductor - the Code permits metallic conduit or a green or bare conductor

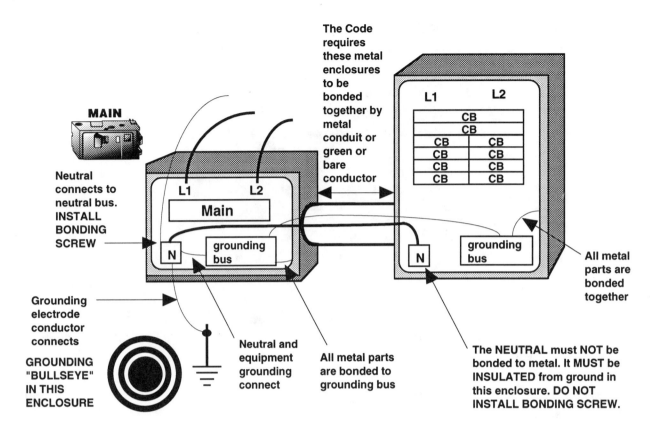

The Code requires these metal enclosures to be bonded together by metal conduit or green or bare conductor

MAIN

Neutral connects to neutral bus. INSTALL BONDING SCREW

L1   L2

Main

N   grounding bus

Grounding electrode conductor connects

GROUNDING "BULLSEYE" IN THIS ENCLOSURE

Neutral and equipment grounding connect

All metal parts are bonded to grounding bus

L1   L2

	CB	
	CB	
CB		CB
CB		CB
CB		CB
CB		CB

N   grounding bus

All metal parts are bonded together

The NEUTRAL must NOT be bonded to metal. It MUST be INSULATED from ground in this enclosure. DO NOT INSTALL BONDING SCREW.

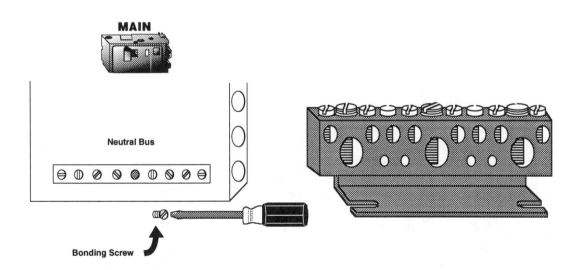

MAIN

Neutral Bus

Bonding Screw

The neutral is only bonded to metal **at the service**; NOT at a sub-panel. This is one of the most violated areas in grounding, mainly because some people simply don't understand the functions of grounding. When incorrectly connecting the neutral to the sub-panel you would have currents flowing on all the metallic equipment connected to the panelboard.

RISER DIAGRAM

The riser diagram specifies the conductors and raceway to be installed. The 2" rigid metal is required as the conduit will be used as a mast and must have the mechanical strength to support the weight of the service entrance drop conductors. In the Northern areas of the United States the weight on the conductors can be very heavy due to ice.

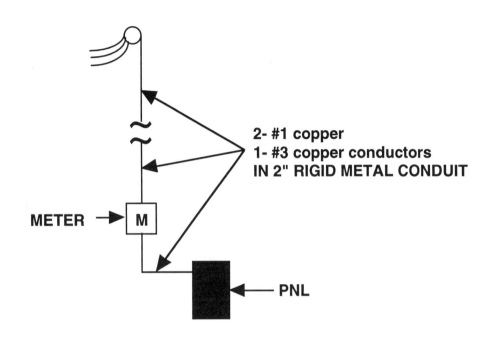

**2- #1 copper
1- #3 copper conductors
IN 2" RIGID METAL CONDUIT**

METER → M

PNL

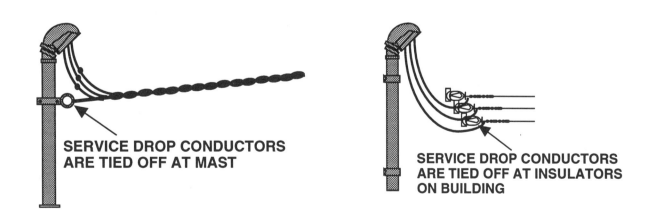

SERVICE DROP CONDUCTORS ARE TIED OFF AT MAST

SERVICE DROP CONDUCTORS ARE TIED OFF AT INSULATORS ON BUILDING

59

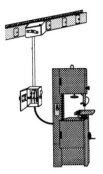

THE LAYOUT

In the real world the **electrician** is called on to design approximately 70% of all electrical work.

In general, the architect, engineer, and designer lay out the larger projects. The electrician is called on for the layout of an add-on, a new piece of equipment for the industry, to wire a new home a friend is building, etc.

The drawings sometimes have no electrical plans, or inadequate electrical plans. A competent electrician can use the floor plans for a new home and layout the home to meet the minimum Code rules. But more important is the electrician that explains to the home owner valuable tips concerning the layout of their new home which exceeds the minimum Code requirements and will provide more convenience, and is designed to meet the future electrical needs.

One must remember when designing there are two routes to choose, the Code required minimum which is used for competitive bidding, and the design which provides more convenience than the Code minimum safety standards, but will be more costly.

In calculating the minimum service size to a house there are only three requirements the Code states you SHALL have:

(1) 3 volt-amps for every square foot of living area.
(2) Two small appliance circuits calculated at 1500va each.
(3) 1500va for the laundry.

The Code does **not** state you SHALL have electric heat, air conditioning, electric water heater, electric clothes dryer, electric cooking equipment, etc. You may have gas appliances or fuel oil heating.

Even today, a 1500 sq.ft. home could have a 60 amp service and meet the Code requirements. A 1500 sq.ft. living area (not carport, garage, unfinished basement) home would generally have three bedrooms and two baths. This is not a smaller size home.

60 AMP

1500 SQ. FT.

The Code requires a 100 amp minimum service if you have **six or more 2-wire branch circuits**. The Code requires a 100 amp minimum if you have a **computed load of 10 kva or more**.

The minimum calculated load to the 1500 sq.ft. house is as follows:

1500 sq.ft. (living area) x 3va	=	4500va
Small appliance 2 x 1500va	=	3000va
Laundry	=	1500va
		9000va

Demand (reduction):

1st 3000va @ 100%	=	3000va
Next 6000va @ 35%	=	2100va
		5100va

The calculated load is 5100va or 5.1 kva, far below the required 10 kva for a 100 amp minimum service size.

The minimum number of 2-wire branch circuits for this home would be:

4500va/120v = 37.5 amps	=	2 - 20 amp circuits
Small appliance	=	2 - 20 amp circuits
Laundry	=	1 - 20 amp circuit
		5 total 2-wire branch circuits

This 1500 sq.ft. home is required to have a minimum of **5** circuits for receptacles throughout the entire house. The 100 amp minimum service requirement is when the house reaches 6 circuits.

The two small appliance circuits are for all the receptacles in the kitchen and dining room. The circuit for the laundry is for the washing machine. The other two circuits are for all the 120 volt receptacles throughout the house. The living room, hallways, bedrooms, bathrooms, etc. are fed from these two required circuits. There is NO limit to the number of receptacles on a branch circuit in a house.

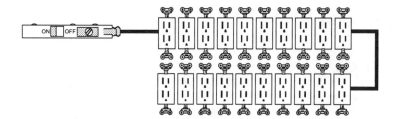

The calculated service load on this home is 5100va/240v = 21.25 amperes. You are not permitted to install a 30 amp service. A **60 amp service** is the minimum requirement. But, do you really want a three bedroom home with a 60 amp service? No way!

The homeowner is not always familiar with electrical plans and future growth electrically. The electrician should spend time with the homeowner pointing out items that will make the home a more convenient place to live.

Communications with the homeowner on the layout of the furniture is very important in the pre-planning stages of determining where the receptacles should be located throughout the house for the greatest flexibility.

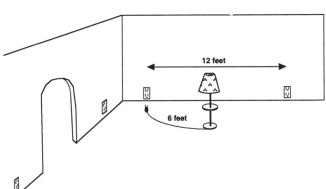

The Code permits receptacles to be spaced a maximum of 12 feet apart. This would allow a light with a six foot cord to reach either receptacle if placed in between them.

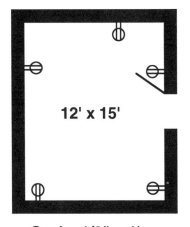

12' x 15'

Scale 1/8" = 1'

One way the electrician can determine the minimum number of receptacles permitted in a room is to measure the perimeter wall space. In the example shown the room is 12' x 15'. The perimeter wall space would be 12' + 12' + 15' + 15' = 54 feet. Divide 54 feet by 12 feet (the Code allowed spacing) = 4.5 or **5** is the minimum number of receptacles permitted in a 12' x 15' room.

Not all electrical appliances and lights have six foot cords. In some cases furniture is hiding the access to a receptacle. Then extension cords are purchased and plugged into the receptacle to reach the electrical appliance, etc.

With better planning and the addition of more receptacles, extension cords can be eliminated in most cases.

The bedroom is a good example of where receptacles can be hidden from view by the furniture. Locating a receptacle under a window where furniture would not be placed is often a good choice of location. A receptacle placed behind the door of a bedroom is a good choice as furniture would not be placed behind the door. Swing the door and plug in your vacuum cleaner.

The bathroom of the house is an area where extra receptacles would NOT be a good choice. With the bathtub, shower, sink, etc. the wet areas make it a good choice to keep receptacles away. Plugging in radios, heaters, etc. have been known to cause electrical accidents. A GFCI receptacle at the sink location is a good idea for plugging in the electric razor or hair dryer.

Good lighting at the mirror is a must in this room.

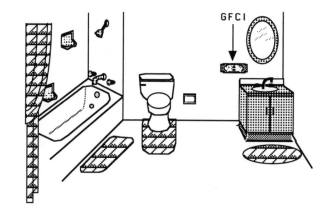

Wiring requirements for the living room also apply to family rooms, dens, and libraries. Too often living rooms are designed without adequate lighting for reading. Lighting should be a major feature in the rooms mentioned. Instead of ceiling lights, split-receptacles are very popular to control table and floor lamps. Wiring provisions for cable TV, telephones, entertainment centers are to be considered.

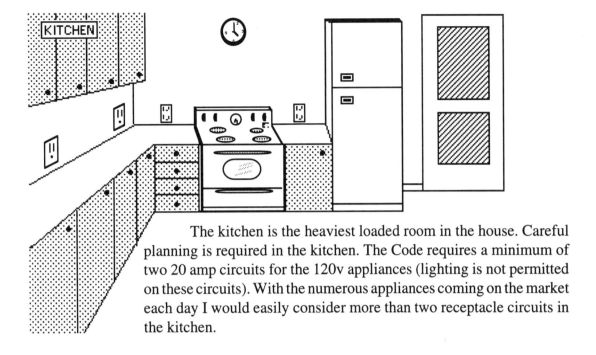

The kitchen is the heaviest loaded room in the house. Careful planning is required in the kitchen. The Code requires a minimum of two 20 amp circuits for the 120v appliances (lighting is not permitted on these circuits). With the numerous appliances coming on the market each day I would easily consider more than two receptacle circuits in the kitchen.

Receptacles are required at each counter wall space 12" or wider. Receptacles above counter tops shall not be spaced farther than 4 feet apart. Receptacles located over 5' 6" don't count as a required receptacle within the spacing. Example would be a receptacle mounted at 7' for a clock.

Separate branch circuits for the refrigerator, disposal, dishwasher or any other heavier load is always good electrical design practice.

A well designed kitchen will have the sink under a window. Good overhead lighting is required in the kitchen so it will shine on work areas used for food preparation. Fluorescent fixtures are commonly used.

If the cooking equipment is electrical, heavier 240v branch circuits must be included.

Hallways, 10 feet or more in length, require at least one receptacle outlet. The length shall be considered along the centerline of the hall without passing through a doorway. Hallways are always a good location for a receptacle as furniture will not be blocking the access. Vacuum cleaners need several locations to plug into.

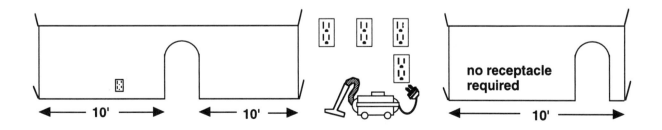

no receptacle required

After planning the number of branch circuits and the location of the receptacles, the actual installation (rough-in) can begin. This must be done before the installation of the drywall.

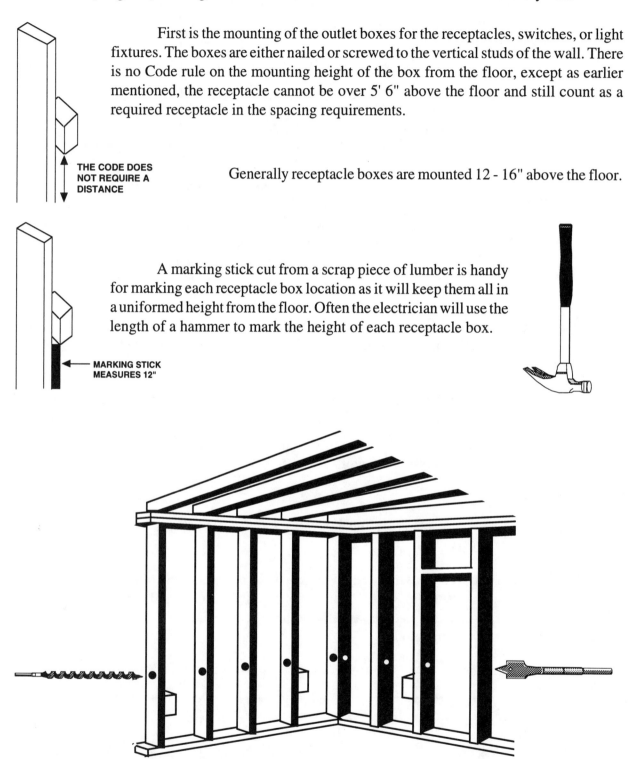

First is the mounting of the outlet boxes for the receptacles, switches, or light fixtures. The boxes are either nailed or screwed to the vertical studs of the wall. There is no Code rule on the mounting height of the box from the floor, except as earlier mentioned, the receptacle cannot be over 5' 6" above the floor and still count as a required receptacle in the spacing requirements.

THE CODE DOES NOT REQUIRE A DISTANCE

Generally receptacle boxes are mounted 12 - 16" above the floor.

A marking stick cut from a scrap piece of lumber is handy for marking each receptacle box location as it will keep them all in a uniformed height from the floor. Often the electrician will use the length of a hammer to mark the height of each receptacle box.

MARKING STICK MEASURES 12"

After the boxes have been mounted holes must be drilled in the studs above the boxes to fish the cable from box to box.

65

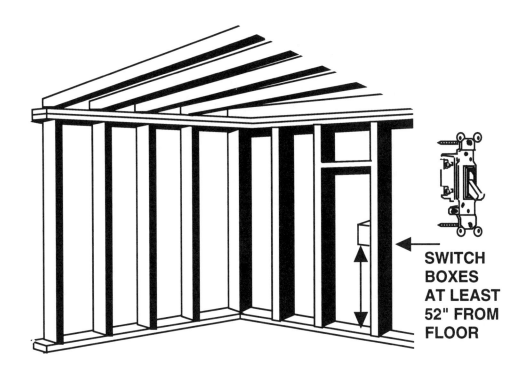

SWITCH BOXES AT LEAST 52" FROM FLOOR

Some drawings show switch box mounting heights at 48" from the floor. Being an electrician over the years has caused me to disagree with this 48" measurement in some cases. When drywall is installed at 48" in height and 12 feet horizontally the box will be located in the taped joint at 48". Same condition exists with the wall that has 4' x 8' paneling laid horizontally as a wainscot for protection of the lower half of the wall, the top trim moulding will cover the box at 48". The bottom of the box should be at least 52" from the floor to stay clear of the 48" of the material being installed, otherwise the joint will fall at the box location. Prior planning before installing boxes is very important in the layout.

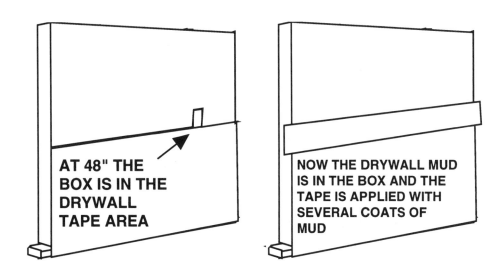

AT 48" THE BOX IS IN THE DRYWALL TAPE AREA

NOW THE DRYWALL MUD IS IN THE BOX AND THE TAPE IS APPLIED WITH SEVERAL COATS OF MUD

66

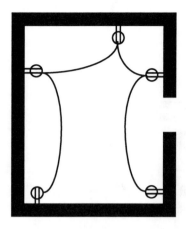

The drawing does not tell the electrician how to run the cable from box to box. The drawing only shows the number of wires to each box.

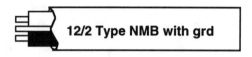

12/2 Type NMB with grd

The field routing of the cable through the studs is left up to the electrician to decide which route is the best.

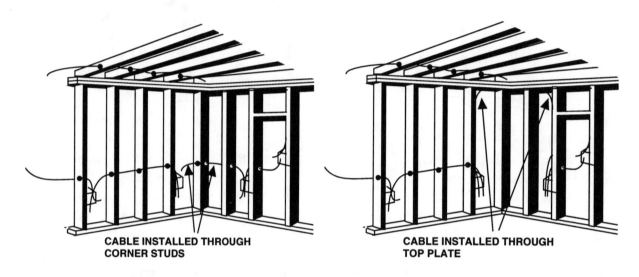

CABLE INSTALLED THROUGH CORNER STUDS

CABLE INSTALLED THROUGH TOP PLATE

Often it is easier to route the cable through the top plate and across the rafters to the next box rather than trying to pull the cable around a sharp corner.

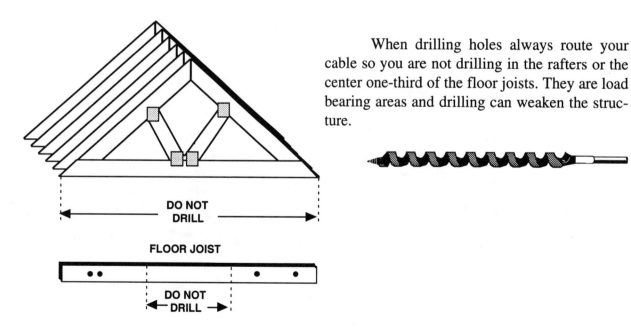

When drilling holes always route your cable so you are not drilling in the rafters or the center one-third of the floor joists. They are load bearing areas and drilling can weaken the structure.

DO NOT DRILL

FLOOR JOIST

DO NOT DRILL

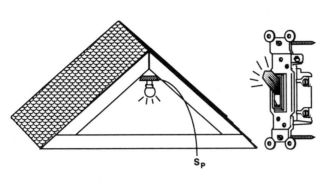

The Code requires a light controlled by a switch in the attic, underfloor space, basement, etc. Good design would require these switches to have a pilot light. Switches that are installed out of sight from lights should have a pilot light to indicate when they are on. A good example is 3-way switches controlling lights in the basement. The extra cost for the pilot light switch will easily be made up by seeing the lights are on.

Back to back boxes or boxes in the same stud chase to opposite rooms are not permitted in fire rated walls. A good example would be a hotel room where a fire in one room could spread to an adjoining room through the boxes even though the wall is fire rated.

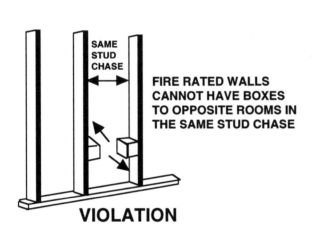

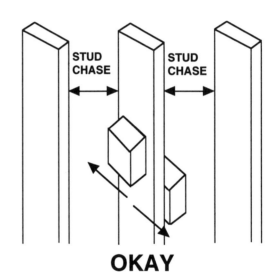

This book "THE ELECTRICAL PLAN READING WORKBOOK" is not designed to give every detail on the step-by-step procedure of service size calculations. You will find in your experiences that each building is different. The same with grounding, short-circuit calculations and transformers. They are subjects themselves and should be carefully studied. I would strongly recommend reading the books I have written on these subjects.

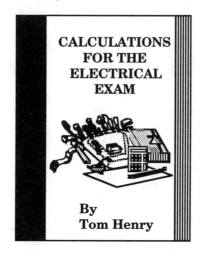

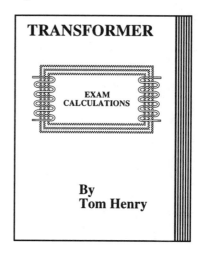

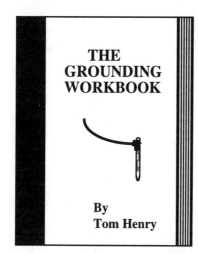

COMMERCIAL - INDUSTRIAL DRAWINGS

Many electricians start their training with wiring houses and during their career there will come a time when they will have the opportunity to wire commercial or industrial.

Commercial buildings can vary from a small office to a large skyscraper.

Very few houses have a feeder or more than one panelboard. With commercial and industrial plans there will generally be several feeders, panels, different types of lighting, motors loads, conduit, etc.

Planning starts before the job has begun and will continue each day until the job is completed. The electrician is required to "field route" the circuits with the least amount of material. Sometimes it will become necessary to alter from the original drawings, but before doing so, the designer of the drawings should be consulted. If changes are made they should be noted on the drawing. This is called "red lined".

The electrician will now be more concerned with the length of circuits to make certain the voltage drop is maintained within the limits. It will be his responsibility to make sure the conduit runs do not interfere with the equipment of the other trades.

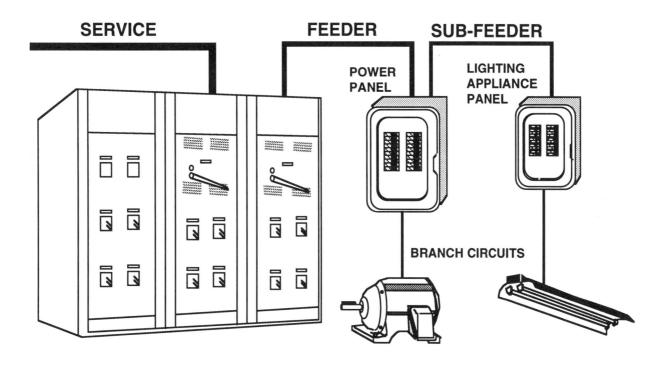

Homeruns on branch circuits should be limited to a maximum of 100 feet for good electrical design. Careful layout of panelboard locations and use of sufficient number of panelboards will avoid the problem of long homeruns with commercial and industrial wiring installation.

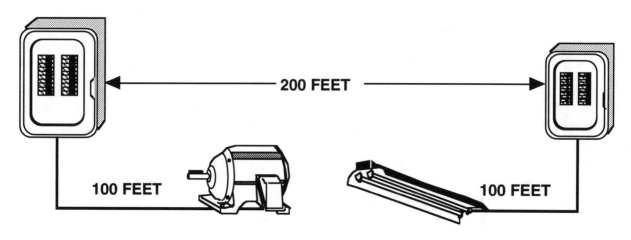

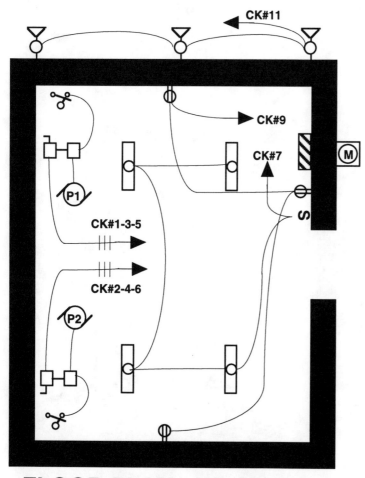

FLOOR PLAN - NO SCALE

Electrical drawings will vary from neat and complete to vague and hard to understand. Very few plans contain every exact detail of the electrical system. A good knowledge of electrical installations which comes from experience will go hand-in-hand with reading electrical plans.

The floor plan drawing shows a lift station with pumps. The floor plan does not give the electrician all the details he needs, such as motor size, wire size, protection size, conduit size, etc. This information will be shown in the panelboard schedule, riser schedule, etc.

SYMBOLS

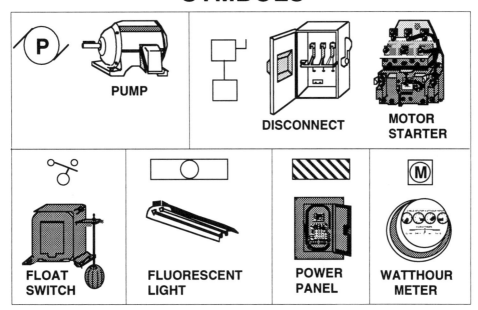

PUMP

DISCONNECT

MOTOR STARTER

FLOAT SWITCH

FLUORESCENT LIGHT

POWER PANEL

WATTHOUR METER

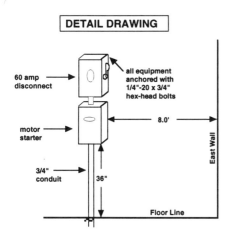

DETAIL DRAWING

60 amp disconnect

all equipment anchored with 1/4"-20 x 3/4" hex-head bolts

motor starter

8.0'

East Wall

3/4" conduit

36"

Floor Line

The floor plan is drawn too small to give all the details necessary for installation. A detail drawing will give more exact measurements and needed information.

Schedules can save the electrician considerable time as they provide the needed information very quickly, rather than reading through all of the specifications.

EQUIPMENT SCHEDULE	
QUANTITY	ITEM
2	10 hp 3ø 208v lift pumps
2	10 hp 3ø motor starters with control transformer
2	60 amp rated disconnects
2	Float switches Model FS-2L14729
4	Quicklight Inc. F-5649 Fluorescent lights
3	20a 120v duplex receptacles
3	Quicklight Inc. M-500-od Mercury lights
1	Single pole switch
1	150 amp 3ø 12 circuit panelboard

The equipment schedule provides information on the materials required for the installation. It does not list conduit, length of wire, fittings, etc. These quantities may vary as the electrician determines the routing of the circuits.

POWER RISER DIAGRAM

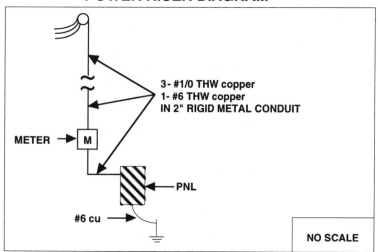

3- #1/0 THW copper
1- #6 THW copper
IN 2" RIGID METAL CONDUIT

METER →

M

PNL

#6 cu →

NO SCALE

The riser diagram gives the needed information on the wire size, conduit size, etc.

CONTROL DIAGRAM

A control transformer reduces the line voltage to 120 volts for the controls.

The control diagram shows a float switch intended for tank operation. When the water reaches "low" level the float switch closes and starts the pump. The pumping action will continue until the water reaches the "high" level.

For sump pumping remove wire"A" and connect as per the dotted line. At "low" level the float switch operates and stops the pumping action. Sump pumping action will not commence until the water reaches the "high" level.

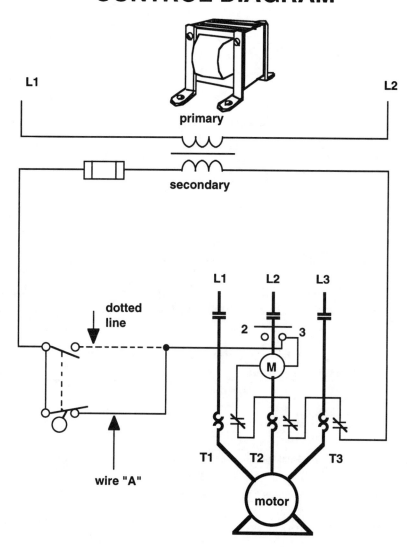

73

PANELBOARD SCHEDULE

MAINS 150 PHASE 3 VOLTS 208/120 AMPERE 150

Circuit Number	Circuit Breaker		Conductor		Serves
	Poles	Amps	Number of	Size	
1	3	80	3	3-#8	Pump #1
2	3	80	3	3-#8	Pump #2
3	—	—	—	—	Pump #1
4	—	—	—	—	Pump #2
5	—	—	—	—	Pump #1
6	—	—	—	—	Pump #2
7	1	20	2	#12	Lights
8	—	—	—	—	Spare
9	1	20	2	#12	Receptacles
10	—	—	—	—	Spare
11	1	20	2	#12	Outside lights
12	—	—	—	—	Spare

The lift station has a 150 amp panelboard with a 208/120v three-phase service. This is called a 4-wire **wye** connected secondary. It is a very common secondary as it can be better balanced as shown below.

Often the electrician is familiar with the connections in the panelboard but cannot visualize the circuit through the transformers.

LOAD BALANCE SCHEDULE

Description	Load	L1	L2	L3	N
Pump #1	11096	3699	3699	3699	0
Pump #2	11096	3699	3699	3699	0
Lights	2400	2400			2400
Receptacles	2400		2400		2400
Outdoor lights	2400			2400	2400
TOTAL	29392	9798	9798	9798	7200

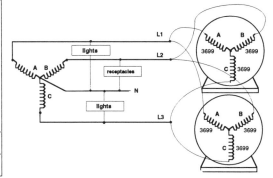

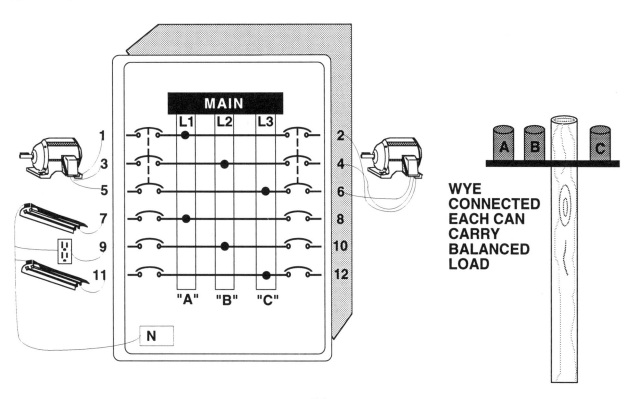

WYE CONNECTED EACH CAN CARRY BALANCED LOAD

PANELBOARD SCHEDULE

Circuit Number	Circuit Breaker		Conductor		Serves
	Poles	Amps	Number of	Size	
1	3	80	3	3-#8	Pump #1
2	3	80	3	3-#8	Pump #2
3					Pump #1
4					Pump #2
5					Pump #1
6					Pump #2
7	1	20	2	#12	Lights
8	1	20	2	#12	Receptacles
9					Spare
10					Spare
11	1	20	2	#12	Outside lights
12					Spare

MAINS 150   PHASE 3   VOLTS 240/120   AMPERE 150

HIGH LEG → 3, 4

HIGH LEG → 8, 10

This page shows the difference with the secondary now **delta** connected.

A delta connected secondary is quite the opposite when it comes to load balancing. Neutral loads can only be connected L1-N or L3-N to transformer "C".

For an example, using the same lift station loads only connected delta 240/120v three-phase. 120v loads cannot connect to **L2 the high-leg**. Transformer "C" is the only one that can carry 120v loads.

HIGH-LEG

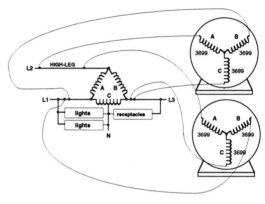

LOAD BALANCE SCHEDULE

Description	Load	L1	L2 (HIGH-LEG)	L3	N
Pump #1	11639	3880	3880	3880	0
Pump #2	11639	3880	3880	3880	0
Lights	2400	2400	HIGH LEG		2400
Receptacles	2400	2400	HIGH LEG		2400
Outdoor lights	2400		HIGH LEG	2400	2400
TOTAL	30478	12560	7760	10160	7200

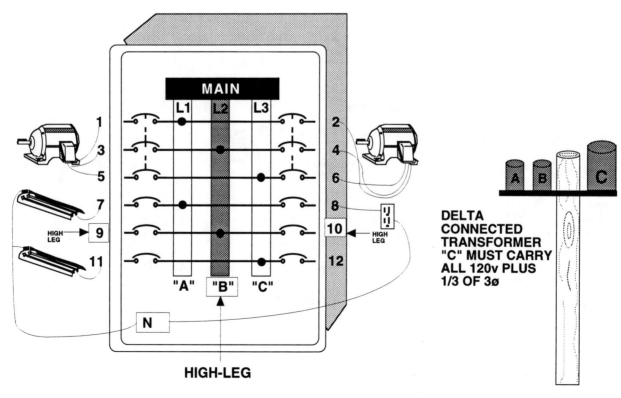

HIGH-LEG

DELTA CONNECTED TRANSFORMER "C" MUST CARRY ALL 120v PLUS 1/3 OF 3ø

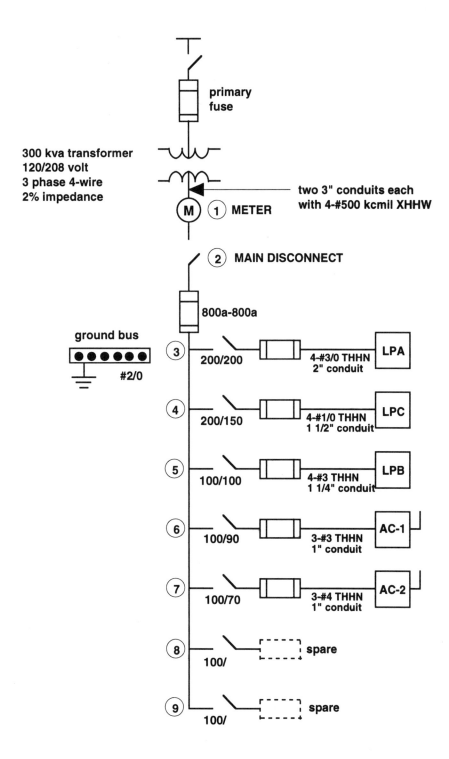

ONE - LINE DRAWING

primary
fuse

300 kva transformer
120/208 volt
3 phase 4-wire
2% impedance

two 3" conduits each
with 4-#500 kcmil XHHW

(M) (1) METER

(2) MAIN DISCONNECT

800a-800a

ground bus

#2/0

(3) 200/200 — 4-#3/0 THHN 2" conduit — LPA

(4) 200/150 — 4-#1/0 THHN 1 1/2" conduit — LPC

(5) 100/100 — 4-#3 THHN 1 1/4" conduit — LPB

(6) 100/90 — 3-#3 THHN 1" conduit — AC-1

(7) 100/70 — 3-#4 THHN 1" conduit — AC-2

(8) 100/ — spare

(9) 100/ — spare

The main distribution panel and another one-line drawing is shown on the following page.

MAIN DISTRIBUTION PANEL   "MDP"
800 AMPERE MLO   120/208 VOLT, 3 PHASE, 4-WIRE

ITEM	EQUIPMENT	SWITCH - FUSE	COMMENTS
1	800a, 120/208v, 3ø, 4 w		INCOMING LINE
2	MAIN SWITCH	800/800 3P	Bolted pressure switch
3	LTNG PNL "LPA"	200/200 3P	LPN-RK FUSES
4	LTNG PNL "LPC"	200/150 3P	LPN-RK FUSES
5	LTNG PNL "LPB"	100/100 3P	LPN-RK FUSES
6	Rooftop unit AC - 1	100/90 3P	LPN-RK FUSES
7	Rooftop unit AC - 2	100/70 3P	LPN-RK FUSES
8	SPARE	100/ 3P	NO FUSES REQUIRED
9	SPARE	100/ 3P	NO FUSES REQUIRED

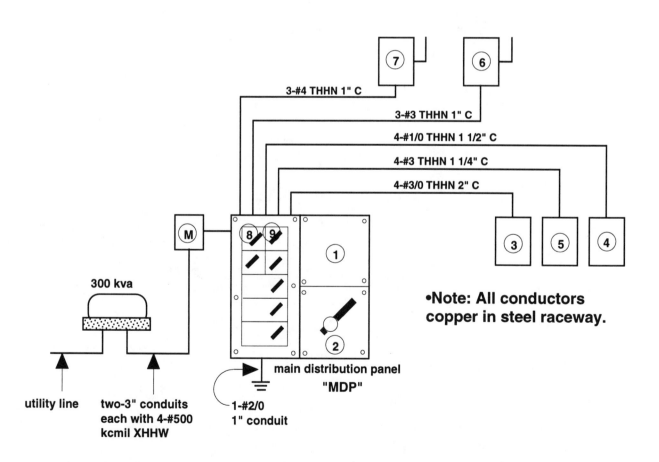

3-#4 THHN 1" C

3-#3 THHN 1" C

4-#1/0 THHN 1 1/2" C

4-#3 THHN 1 1/4" C

4-#3/0 THHN 2" C

•Note: All conductors
copper in steel raceway.

300 kva

main distribution panel
"MDP"

1-#2/0
1" conduit

utility line

two-3" conduits
each with 4-#500
kcmil XHHW

SHORT-CIRCUIT CALCULATIONS

Whereas overload currents occur at rather modest levels, the short-circuit or fault current can be many hundreds of times larger than the normal operating current. A high level fault may be 50,000 amps or more. If not cut off within a few thousandths of a second, there can be severe damage, melting of conductors, arcing and fires.

The point to point method of calculating short-circuit currents is based on computation of the two main circuit impedance parameters, transformers and conductors. Of these two components, the transformer is generally the major short-circuit current factor for faults near the service entrance. The percent of impedance of the transformer can vary considerably. The transformer specification of the drawing should always be checked.

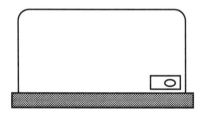

Transformer impedance (Z) helps determine what the short circuit current will be at the transformer secondary. Transformer impedance is determined as follows:

The transformer secondary is shorted. Voltage is applied to the primary which causes full load current to flow in the secondary. The applied voltage divided by the rated primary voltage is the impedance of the transformer.

480v RATED PRIMARY

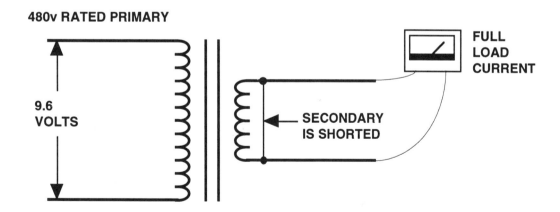

For a 480 volt rated primary, if 9.6 volts causes secondary full load current to flow through the shorted secondary, the transformer impedance is 9.6/480 = .02 = 2% impedance.

First step is to determine the transformer full load amperes from either the nameplate or by using the formula:

$$3\phi \text{ Transformer } I = \frac{\text{kva x } 1000}{E \text{ x } 1.732}$$

$$1\phi \text{ Transformer } I = \frac{\text{kva x } 1000}{E}$$

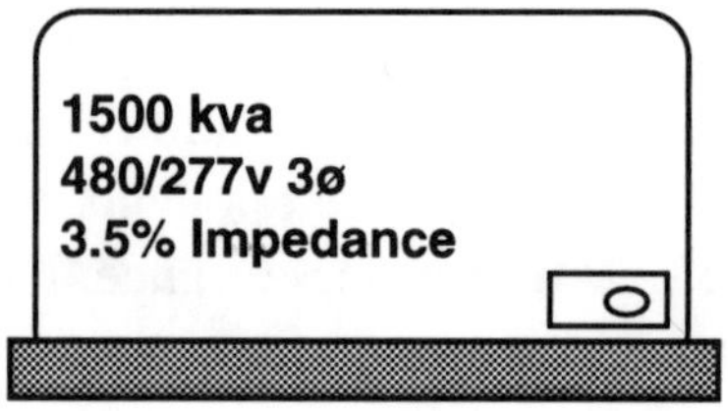

1500 kva
480/277v 3ø
3.5% Impedance

$$\frac{1500 \text{ x } 1000}{480v \text{ x } 1.732} = 1804 \text{ amperes}$$

Next step is to find the muliplier. Divide 100 by the % of impedance. 100/3.5% = 28.57

The available short-circuit current from this transformer would be 1804 amperes x 28.57 = 51,504 amperes.

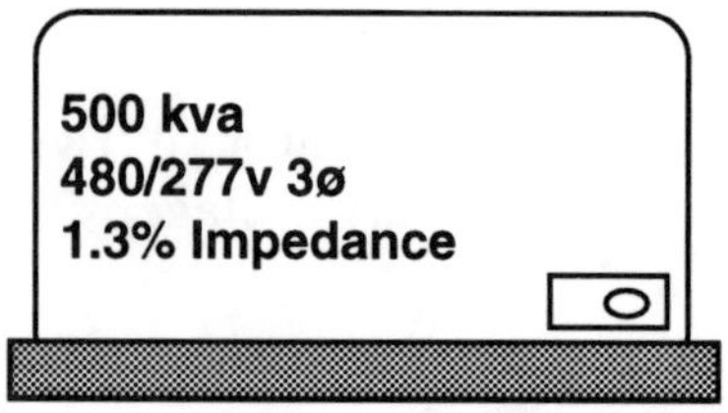

500 kva
480/277v 3ø
1.3% Impedance

$$\frac{500 \text{ x } 1000}{480v \text{ x } 1.732} = 601 \text{ amperes}$$

The multiplier is 100/1.3% = 76.9 x 601 amperes = 46,217 amperes short-circuit current.

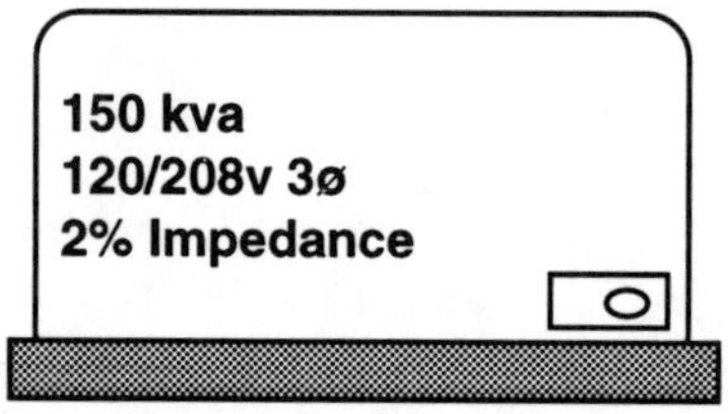

150 kva
120/208v 3ø
2% Impedance

$$\frac{150 \text{ x } 1000}{208 \text{ x } 1.732} = 416 \text{ amperes}$$

The multiplier is 100/2% = 50 x 416 amperes = 20,800 amperes short-circuit current.

Neglecting conductor impedances simplifies short-circuit calculations in circuits.

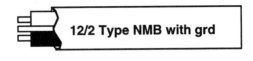

The 120 volt branch circuit shown below is 50 feet in distance from the source to the load. This circuit would contain 100 feet of conductor. A #12 solid conductor has a resistance of 1.93Ω per thousand feet. 1.93Ω x .050' = .0965Ω per 50 feet or .193Ω for 100 feet. The load has a resistance of 7.5Ω. The total resistance in the circuit is .0965 + .0965 + 7.5 = 7.693Ω.

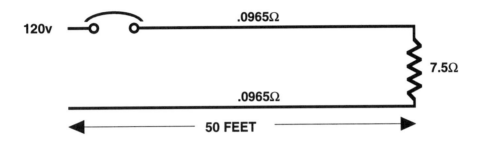

To find the current flowing in this circuit divide 120v by 7.693Ω = 15.6 amps.

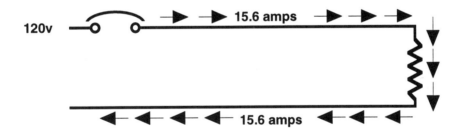

The 15.6 amps is the normal current. The 20 amp current rating of a breaker is the current level which the breaker is designed to carry continuously. The second type of rating given to a breaker is the interrupting capacity (AIC). It is the highest short-circuit current at a rated voltage that the breaker can safely interrupt. If a fault current exceeds the interrupting rating of the breaker it can be damaged or destroyed. Severe equipment damage and personal injury can result.

Checking the drawings for short-circuit calculations is a very important area for the plans examiner.

Short-circuits are a result of an abnormal occurrence which causes the current to take a path outside the usual conducting path through the resistance of the load.

 An example an electrician can relate to would be cutting into the black and white wire at the same time with the power on.

If the wire was accidentally cut at the load the circuit would only have the resistance of the wire as the load resistance is bypassed through the pliers which has less resistance.

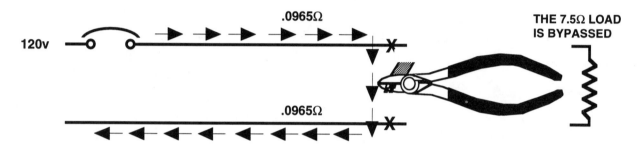

The resistance of the circuit is .0965Ω + .0965Ω = .193Ω. I = 120v/.193Ω = 622 amps.

If the wire was cut 4 feet from the breaker the circuit would see over 7000 amperes!

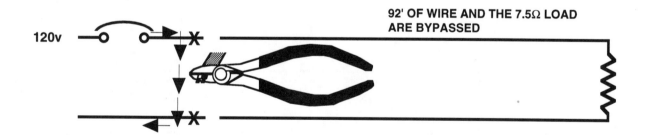

The resistance of the circuit is 1.93Ω per thousand feet x .008 feet of wire = .01544Ω.

I = 120v/.01544Ω = 7,772 amperes.

Because the load is bypassed, a very large magnitude of fault current can occur. In recent years many utility companies have increased their generating capacity and consequently available short-circuit currents have also increased. Newer transformers with lower impedance ratings have allowed for greater magnitudes of fault current. These factors made the proper selection of an overcurrent device with a proper interrupting rating extremely critical.

A ground fault is a phase (line) conductor contacting the metal raceway enclosure (conduit), motor frame, etc.

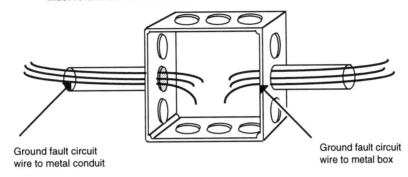

Ground fault caused by conductor insulation breakdown allowing circuit current to flow into metal conduit or metal box - This current must return to the fuse or breaker

Ground fault circuit wire to metal conduit

Ground fault circuit wire to metal box

A fault may start as a ground fault and develop into a short circuit or vice versa. The first situation is the more common. It is very important to understand the difference between a ground fault and a short circuit as it is a more serious condition to protect against an insulation failure of a conductor to a metal enclosure.

When a fault occurs in a circuit, it is only during the time period while the fault exists that a potential hazard is present. That is why it is so important to clear the fault as quickly as possible by blowing the fuse or tripping the circuit breaker.

The fault current must return to the overcurrent protection (fuse or circuit breaker) in order to blow the fuse or trip the breaker. The grounding circuit is the return path to the overcurrent device.

Without this grounding circuit, a fault current will generate heat and eventually enough heat damage will cause the insulation to breakdown causing a short circuit which will cause the fuse to blow or the circuit breaker to trip.

A ground fault that is not allowed to clear itself is a very dangerous situation. A fault current may exist for minutes, hours, or days. During this time that the fault is uncleared, faults can cause a fire or even a fatal shock. Electrical accident statistics have proven that many personal injuries are caused by electric shock as a result of making contact with metal that is not normally energized. An effective grounding path would eliminate these injuries.

The interrupting rating of most branch-circuit, molded case, circuit breakers like a 20 amp used in residential services are 10,000 amperes. The rating is usually expressed as "10,000 AIC" (AIC is the abbreviation for "amperes interrupting capacity.") Larger circuit breakers may have ratings of 14,000 or higher. Current-limiting fuses have an interrupting capacity of 200,000 amperes.

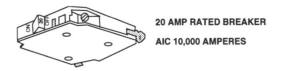

20 AMP RATED BREAKER
AIC 10,000 AMPERES

82

The maximum available fault current must be known in order to comply with Code Section 110-9. The transformer is generally the major short-circuit current factor for faults near the service entrance. Given the full-load transformer secondary amperage and % impedance of a transformer the available short-circuit current delivered at the secondary terminals can be calculated.

Short-circuit Currents Available From Transformers

	KVA	Full Load Amps	% Impedance	Short-circuit amps
240/120v 1ø	25	104	1.6	11,431
	50	209	1.7	21,065
	100	417	1.6	42,779
208/120v 3ø	150	417	2.0	23,166
	500	1388	2.0	77,111
	1000	2776	5.0	88,127
	2500	6950	5.0	154,444
480/277v 3ø	150	181	1.2	16,759
	500	601	1.3	51,368
	1000	1203	5.0	38,180
	2500	3007	5.0	66,822

Motors also add current to the short-circuit currents.

To adequately protect components, it is very important that the overcurrent protective device be current-limiting. Current-limiting overcurrent devices cuts the short-circuit current off before the first full cycle can reach its maximum value.

If an overcurrent device cuts off a short-circuit current in less than one-half cycle, before it reaches its total available (and highly destructive) value, the overcurrent device is a "current limiting" device.

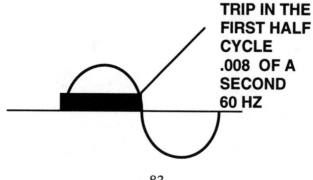

TRIP IN THE FIRST HALF CYCLE .008 OF A SECOND 60 HZ

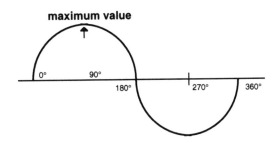
maximum value

0° 90° 180° 270° 360°

With a ground-fault condition, the higher the faulted current flows the quicker the breaker will trip. If the breaker does not trip quickly and the current remains for several cycles you are generating heat which will cause damage.

The chart below shows the approximate current that conductors can carry during a ground-fault or short-circuit condition without damage to the insulation.

Copper, 75° C Thermoplastic Insulated Cable Damage Table

Copper Wire Size 75° C Thermo-plastic	Maximum Short-Circuit Withstand Current In Amperes For					
	1/8 Cycle	1/4 Cycle	1/2 Cycle	1 Cycle	2 Cycles	3 Cycles
#14	4800	3400	2400	1700	1200	1000
#12	7600	5400	3800	2700	1900	1550
#10	12000	8500	6020	4300	3000	2450
#8	19200	13500	9600	6800	4800	3900
#6	30400	21500	15200	10800	7600	6200
#4	48400	34200	24200	17100	12100	9900

A #12 conductor with 75°C insulation can withstand 3800 amps but only for 1/2 of a cycle and on a 60 cycle system that equals eight thousandths of one second which is a very short time period.

Available short-circuit current and clearing time of the overcurrent device must be considered so the withstand rating of the conductor is not exceeded.

The 75°C conductor has three withstand classifications:

(1) INSULATION DAMAGE 150°C or 302°F
(2) TERMINAL DAMAGE   250°C or 482°F
(3) MELTING   1083°C or 1981°F

Shown below are examples using a #6 THW (75°C) conductor which has a normal ampacity of 65 amps.

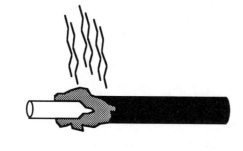

INSULATION DAMAGE

**#6 THW can withstand
15,218 amps for 1/2 cycle**

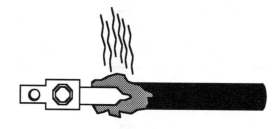

**TERMINAL DAMAGE
(loosening of lugs)**

**#6 THW can withstand
22,090 amps for 1/2 cycle**

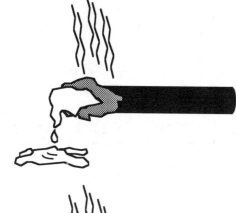

MELTING

**#6 THW can withstand
39,704 amps for 1/2 cycle**

**IF THE CURRENT CONTINUED
FOR 5 SECONDS (300 cycles)
THE #6 THW WOULD MELT AT
1620 AMPS**

Shown on the next two pages is a floor plan **R-3344** for a restaurant. The restaurant has a single-phase and a three-phase panel. Also shown on the following pages will be the service riser, panel schedules and load balancing schedule.

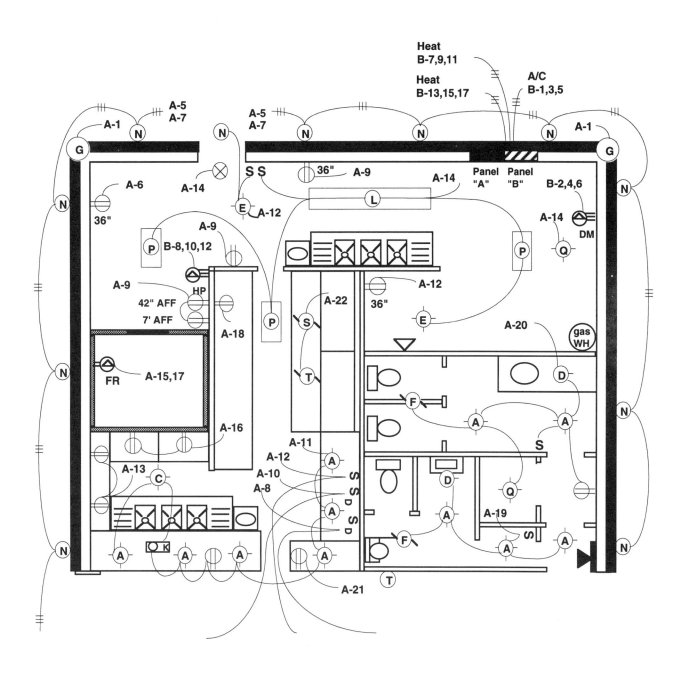

(THIS PLAN IS CONTINUED ON THE NEXT PAGE)

PART "B" OF PLAN

R-3344

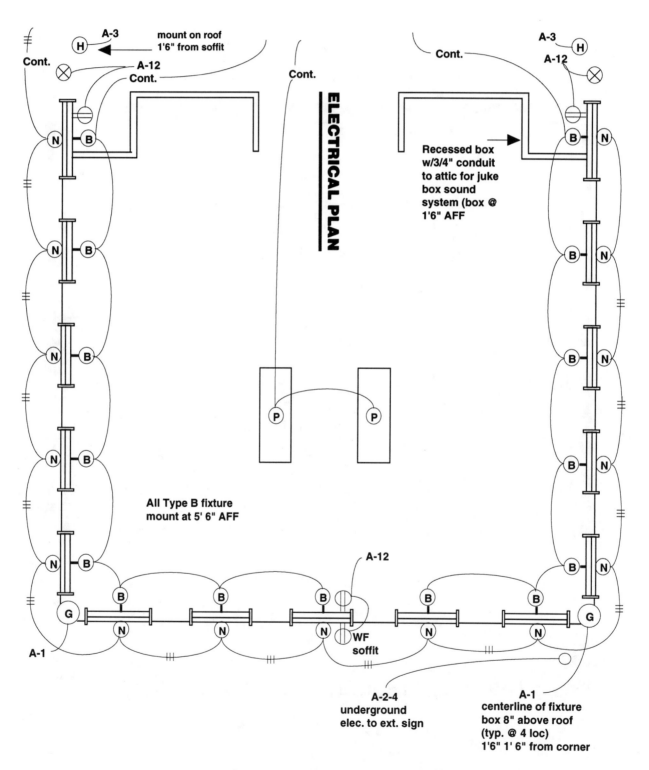

mount on roof 1'6" from soffit

Cont.

A-3

A-12
Cont.

Cont.

ELECTRICAL PLAN

A-3

A-12

Cont.

Recessed box w/3/4" conduit to attic for juke box sound system (box @ 1'6" AFF

All Type B fixture mount at 5' 6" AFF

A-12

A-1

WF soffit

A-2-4 underground elec. to ext. sign

A-1 centerline of fixture box 8" above roof (typ. @ 4 loc) 1'6" 1' 6" from corner

PLAN R-3344 SERVICE RISER

2 - #300 kcmil THW
1 - #2/0 THW(hi-leg)
1 - #1 THW Neutral
2 1/2" conduit

M

GUTTER

2-#2/0 THW
1-#1 THW Neutral
1 1/2" conduit

3-#4/0 THW
1-#2 THW Neutral
2" conduit

A

B

Panel "A"
1ø 240/120v
200 amp bus
175 amp main

Panel "B"
3ø 240v
225 amp bus
225 amp main

B

175a fused non-time
delay to A/C unit

60a fused non-time
delay to heat

60a fused non-time
delay to heat

•Note: A/C 24 kva 3ø
2-18 kva HEATERS

LIGHTING FIXTURE SCHEDULE R-3344				
Symbol	Quantity	Manufacturer #	Mounting	Lamps
(A)	11	Nicelite Co. CM-43572	recessed	100w
(B)	15	Brightlite Co. L-s 23975	bracket	60w
(C)	1	Nicelite Co. CM-881327	recessed	100w
(D)	2	Baker B-7604r	bracket	2-40w
(E)	2	Star Light CM-43211	surface	100w
(F)	2	Blowtime Inc. f-47338	recessed	exhaust fan
(G)	4	Roof lts. Inc. R-67531	surface	3-150w
(H)	2	Roof lts. Inc. R-82209-r	surface	500w
(K)	1	Quicklite Inc. F-5649	surface	2-F20CW
(L)	1	Quicklite Inc. F-7571	surface	1-75w CW
(N)	26	Star Light WD-5642	surface	100w
(P)	5	Quicklite Inc. F-8071r	recessed	4-40w CW
(Q)	2	Star Light CM-11182	surface	100w
⊗	2	3-Star Security X-2376	surface	25w
(S)	1	Blowtime Inc. f-1500-w	recessed	exhaust fan
(T)	1	Blowtime Inc. f-812-w	recessed	exhaust fan

PANEL "A" Single-phase 240/120 volt

PANELBOARD SCHEDULE R-3344

MAINS 175 **PHASE** 1 **VOLTS** 240/120 **AMPERE** 200

Circuit Number	Circuit Breaker		Conductor		Serves
	Poles	Amps	Number of	Size	
1	1	20	2	#12	4-corner roof lights
2	1	20	2	#12	Pole Sign
3	1	20	2	#12	Two center roof lights
4	1	20	2	#12	Pole Sign
5	1	20	2	#12	Exterior bracket lights
6	1	20	2	#12	Freezer
7	1	20	2	#12	Exterior bracket lights
8	1	20	2	#12	Dining Room lights
9	1	20	2	#12	Food warmer & hood
10	1	20	2	#12	Dining Room lights
11	1	20	2	#12	Lights @ bar & recpt.
12	1	20	2	#12	Work area lts. & recpt.
13	1	20	2	#12	Coffee Urn & Tea
14	1	20	2	#12	Kitchen & Storage Lts.
15	2	20	2	#12	Walk-in-cooler
16	1	20	2	#12	Ice machine/glass froster
17	2	20	2	#12	Walk-in-cooler
18	1	20	2	#12	Dough roller
19	1	20	2	#12	Rest room lights & fan
20	1	20	2	#12	Rest room lights & fan
21	1	20	2	#12	Cash register
22	1	20	2	#12	Fans
23					SPARE
24					SPARE

PANEL "B" Three-phase 240 volt

PANELBOARD SCHEDULE R-3344

MAINS 225 **PHASE** 3 **VOLTS** 240/120 **AMPERE** 225

Circuit Number	Circuit Breaker		Conductor		Serves
	Poles	Amps	Number of	Size	
1	3	175	3	#2	Air-conditioner
2	3	20	3	#12	Dough mixer
3	3	175	3	#2	Air-conditioner
4	3	20	3	#12	Dough mixer
5	3	175	3	#2	Air-conditioner
6	3	20	3	#12	Dough mixer
7	3	60	3	#6	Electric Heater
8	3	20	3	#12	Electric hot plate
9	3	60	3	#6	Electric Heater
10	3	20	3	#12	Electric hot plate
11	3	60	3	#6	Electric Heater
12	3	20	3	#12	Electric hot plate
13	3	60	3	#6	Electric Heater
14					SPARE
15	3	60	3	#6	Electric Heater
16					SPARE
17	3	60	3	#6	Electric Heater
18					SPARE
19					SPARE
20					SPARE
21					SPARE
22					SPARE
23					SPARE
24					SPARE

LOAD BALANCING - DELTA

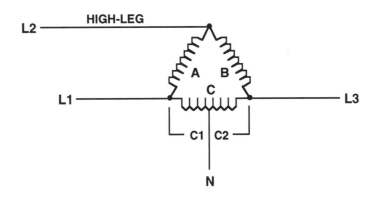

LOAD BALANCE SCHEDULE

TRANSFORMER

A	B	C	DESCRIPTION
6000	6000	6000	18 kva heater 3ø 240v
6000	6000	6000	18 kva heater 3ø 240v
8000	8000	8000	24 kva A/C 3ø 240v
2000	2000	2000	6 kva hot plate 3ø 240v
600	600	600	1800va dough machine 3ø 240v

		C1	C2	
		6000	6000	Lights and recpts. 1ø 120v
		2000	2000	Walk-in cooler 1ø 240v
		1800	1800	Corner roof lights 1ø 120v
		1700	1700	Pole mounted sign 1ø 120v
		1500		Coffee & tea 1ø 120v
			1000	Center roof sign 1ø 120v
			830	Freezer 1ø 120v
			830	Glass froster 1ø 120v
		830	830	Exhaust hood fans 1ø 120v
		830		Ice machine 1ø 120v
			580	Glass washer 1ø 120v
		530	530	Bath exhaust fans 1ø 120v
		530		Hot plate hood 1ø 120v

A	B	C	
22600va	**22600va**	**54420va**	**Load per transformer Total load = 99620va**

NEUTRAL CALCULATION - DELTA

6000	6000	Lights and recpts. 1ø 120v
	~~2000~~	~~2000~~	~~Walk-in cooler 1ø 240v~~
1800	1800	Corner roof lights 1ø 120v
1700	1700	Pole mounted sign 1ø 120v
1500		Coffee & tea 1ø 120v
	1000	Center roof sign 1ø 120v
	830	Freezer 1ø 120v
	830	Glass froster 1ø 120v
830	830	Exhaust hood fans 1ø 120v
830		Ice machine 1ø 120v
	580	Glass washer 1ø 120v
530	530	Bath exhaust fans 1ø 120v
530		Hot plate hood 1ø 120v
13720 va	**14100va**	

•NOTE: Walk-in cooler is **not** a neutral load at 240v.

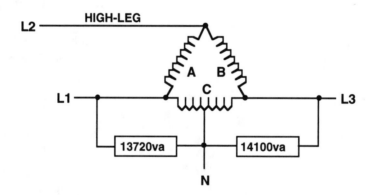

The maximum load on the neutral conductor would be 14100va/120v = **117.5 amperes**.

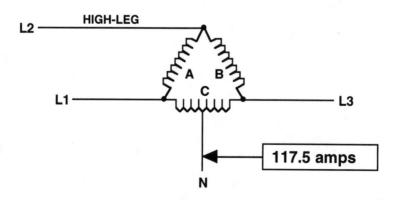

92

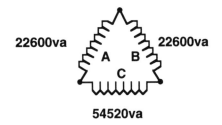

22600va/240v = 94a
54520va/240v = 227a

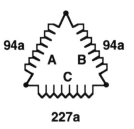

LINE LOADS

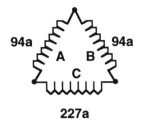

FORMULA FOR UNBALANCED DELTA CURRENT:

L1 current = Phase A + Phase C, divided by 2, times 1.732
L2 current = Phase A + Phase B, divided by 2, times 1.732
L3 current = Phase B + Phase C, divided by 2, times 1.732

L1 current = 94a + 227a = 321a/2 = 160.5a x 1.732 = 278a
L2 current = 94a + 94a = 188a/2 =   94a x 1.732 = 163a
L3 current = 94a + 227a = 321a/2 = 160.5a x 1.732 = 278a

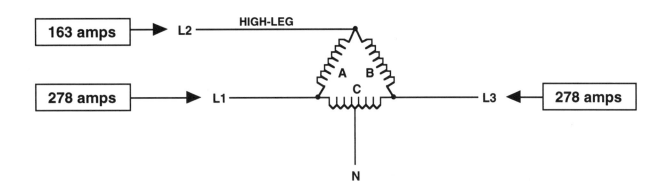

Total load is 99,620va/240v/1.732 = 240 amps.

93

SIZING THE CONDUCTORS - DELTA

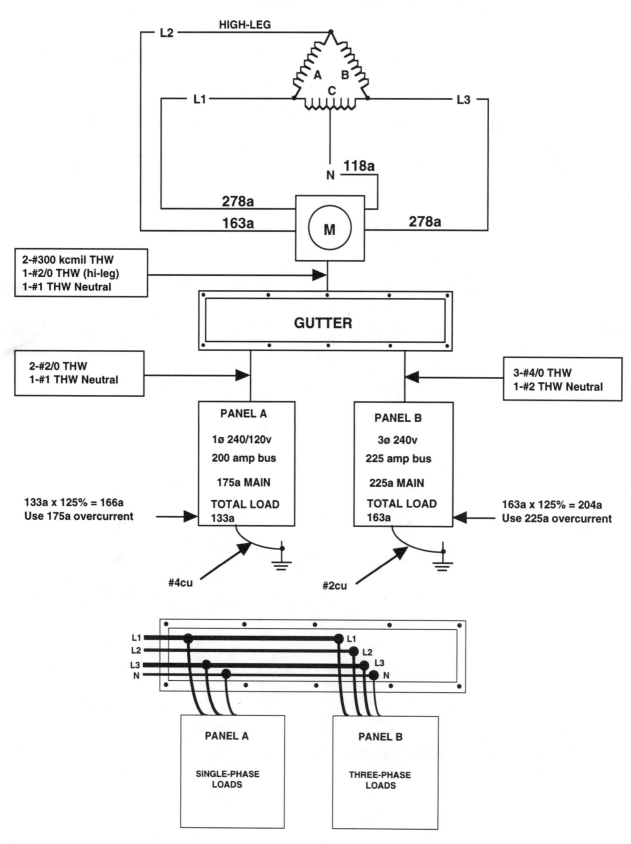

HIGH-LEG

L2

A   B

C

L1   L3

N   118a

278a

163a   M   278a

2-#300 kcmil THW
1-#2/0 THW (hi-leg)
1-#1 THW Neutral

GUTTER

2-#2/0 THW
1-#1 THW Neutral

3-#4/0 THW
1-#2 THW Neutral

PANEL A	PANEL B
1ø 240/120v	3ø 240v
200 amp bus	225 amp bus
175a MAIN	225a MAIN
TOTAL LOAD	TOTAL LOAD
133a	163a

133a x 125% = 166a
Use 175a overcurrent

163a x 125% = 204a
Use 225a overcurrent

#4cu   #2cu

L1   L1
L2   L2
L3   L3
N   N

PANEL A	PANEL B
SINGLE-PHASE LOADS	THREE-PHASE LOADS

94

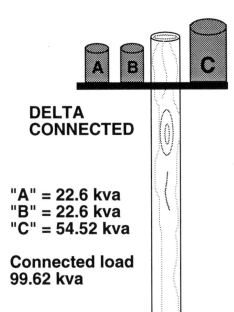

DELTA
CONNECTED

"A" = 22.6 kva
"B" = 22.6 kva
"C" = 54.52 kva

**Connected load
99.62 kva**

The delta connection will require one larger transformer ("C") which carries one-third of all three-phase loads plus all of the 120 volt loads. Only transformer "C" can provide 120 volts.

The following pages will show the same loads only now they are 208/120v three-phase wye connected. With the wye all three phases have a neutral connection and will provide a more equal balancing among the three transformers.

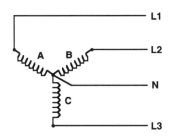

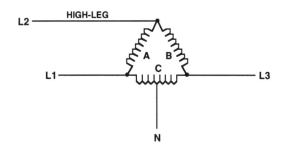

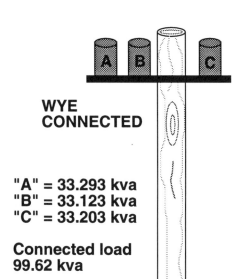

WYE
CONNECTED

"A" = 33.293 kva
"B" = 33.123 kva
"C" = 33.203 kva

**Connected load
99.62 kva**

The wye connection provides an equal distribution of the 120 volt loads among all three transfomers.

LOAD BALANCING - WYE

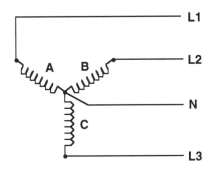

LOAD BALANCE SCHEDULE

TRANSFORMER

A	B	C	DESCRIPTION
6000	6000	6000	18 kva heater 3ø 208v
6000	6000	6000	18 kva heater 3ø 208v
8000	8000	8000	24 kva A/C 3ø 208v
2000	2000	2000	6 kva hot plate 3ø 208v
600	600	600	1800va dough machine 3ø 208v
4000	4000	4000	Lights and recpts. 1ø 120v
2000	2000		Walk-in cooler 1ø 208v
1200	1200	1200	Corner roof lights 1ø 120v
1133	1133	1133	Pole mounted sign 1ø 120v
		1500	Coffee & tea 1ø 120v
1000			Center roof sign 1ø 120v
	830		Freezer 1ø 120v
		830	Glass froster 1ø 120v
830	830		Exhaust hood fans 1ø 120v
		830	Ice machine 1ø 120v
		580	Glass washer 1ø 120v
	530	530	Bath exhaust fans 1ø 120v
530			Hot plate hood 1ø 120v
__33293va__	__33123va__	__33203va__	Load per transformer Total load = 99619va

96

NEUTRAL CALCULATION - WYE

A	B	C	
4000	4000	4000	Lights and recpts. 1ø 120v
~~2000~~	~~2000~~		~~Walk-in cooler 1ø 208v~~
1200	1200	1200	Corner roof lights 1ø 120v
1133	1133	1133	Pole mounted sign 1ø 120v
		1500	Coffee & tea 1ø 120v
1000			Center roof sign 1ø 120v
	830		Freezer 1ø 120v
		830	Glass froster 1ø 120v
830	830		Exhaust hood fans 1ø 120v
		830	Ice machine 1ø 120v
		580	Glass washer 1ø 120v
	530	530	Bath exhaust fans 1ø 120v
530			Hot plate hood 1ø 120v
8693va	**8523va**	**10603va**	

•NOTE: Walk-in cooler is **not** a neutral load at 208v.

Transformer "A" = 8693va/120v = 72.4 amps
Transformer "B" = 8523va/120v = 71 amps
Transformer "C" = 10603va/120v = 88.3 amps

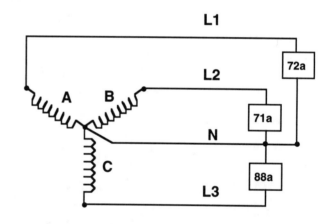

The maximum load on the neutral conductor would be **88 amperes**.

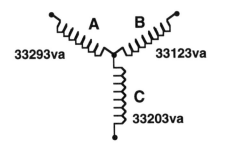

$$33293va/120v = 277a$$

$$33123va/120v = 276a$$

$$33203va/120v = 277a$$

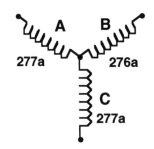

LINE LOADS

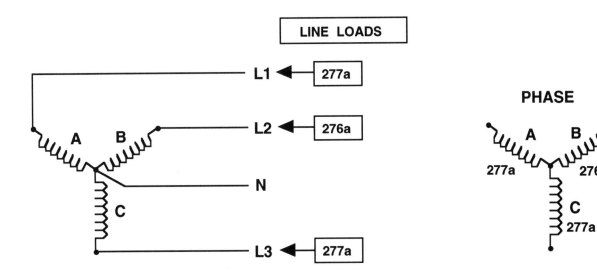

The line amps are the same as the phase amps wye-connected.

L1	L2	L3
33293va	33123va	33203va = **99619 va total**

99619va/208v/1.732 = **276.5 amps**

98

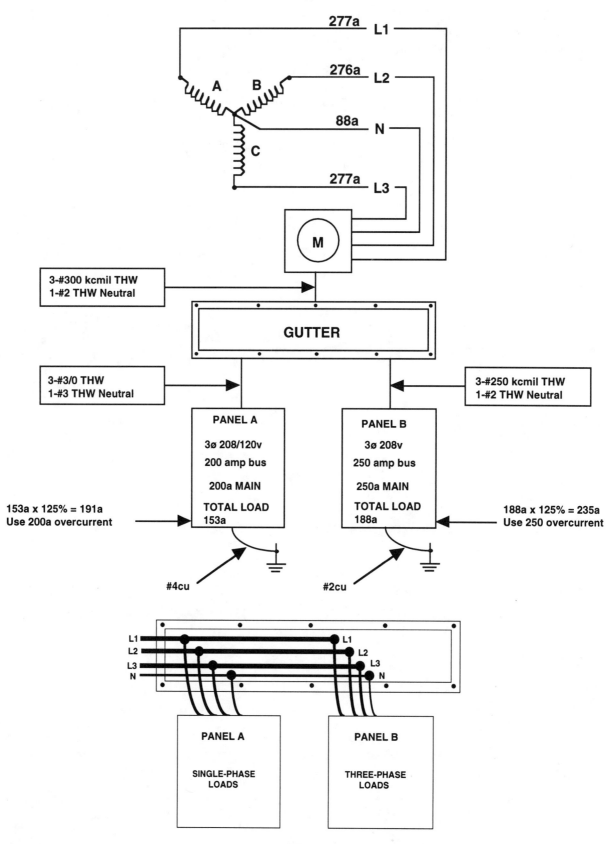

SIZING THE CONDUCTORS - WYE

277a L1

276a L2

A   B

88a N

C

277a L3

M

3-#300 kcmil THW
1-#2 THW Neutral

GUTTER

3-#3/0 THW
1-#3 THW Neutral

3-#250 kcmil THW
1-#2 THW Neutral

PANEL A

3ø 208/120v

200 amp bus

200a MAIN

TOTAL LOAD
153a

PANEL B

3ø 208v

250 amp bus

250a MAIN

TOTAL LOAD
188a

153a x 125% = 191a
Use 200a overcurrent

188a x 125% = 235a
Use 250 overcurrent

#4cu

#2cu

L1
L2
L3
N

L1
L2
L3
N

PANEL A

SINGLE-PHASE
LOADS

PANEL B

THREE-PHASE
LOADS

Different manufacturers of panelboards make different sizes of ampere ratings and spaces for single-phase and three-phase panelboards.

Manufacturer "X"

SINGLE-PHASE	
Ampere Rating	**Spaces**
60a	12-18-24
100a	12-18-24
150a	30-36-42
225a	12-18-24-30-36-42

Manufacturer "Y"

SINGLE-PHASE	
Ampere Rating	**Spaces**
100a	12-20
125a	30-42
150a	30-42
175a	30-42
200a	30-42
225a	30-42

Manufacturer "X"

THREE-PHASE	
Ampere Rating	**Spaces**
100a	12-18-24-30-36-42
150a	12-18-24-30-36-42
225a	12-18-24-30-36-42
250a	12-18-24-30-36-42
400a	12-18-24-30-36-42
600a	12-18-24-30-36-42

Manufacturer "X"

THREE-PHASE	
Ampere Rating	**Spaces**
100a	12-24-30-42
110a	12-24-30-42
125a	12-24-30-42
150a	12-24-30-42
175a	12-24-30-42
200a	12-24-30-42
225a	12-24-30-42
250a	12-24-30-42
300a	12-24-30-42
350a	12-24-30-42
400a	12-24-30-42
600a	12-24-30-42

SLAB DRAWING

      The following pages show drawings with conduits installed in the concrete slab. The conduits must be secured so they don't move during the pouring of the concrete. The ends of the stub-ups must be capped to prevent concrete from entering.

TYPICAL STUB-UP DETAIL

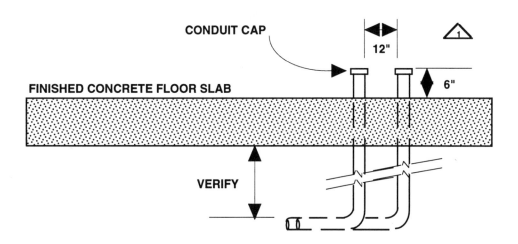

GENERAL NOTES:
⚠ **1. ALL CONDUIT SHOWN IN DETAILS ARE 3/4" UNLESS OTHERWISE NOTED.**

SLAB DRAWING

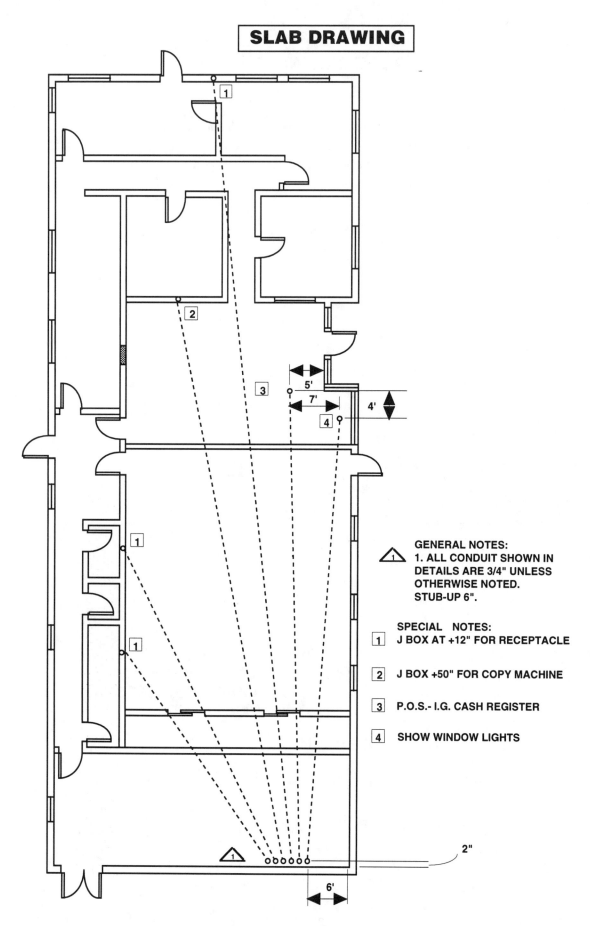

GENERAL NOTES:
1. ALL CONDUIT SHOWN IN DETAILS ARE 3/4" UNLESS OTHERWISE NOTED. STUB-UP 6".

SPECIAL NOTES:

1. J BOX AT +12" FOR RECEPTACLE

2. J BOX +50" FOR COPY MACHINE

3. P.O.S.- I.G. CASH REGISTER

4. SHOW WINDOW LIGHTS

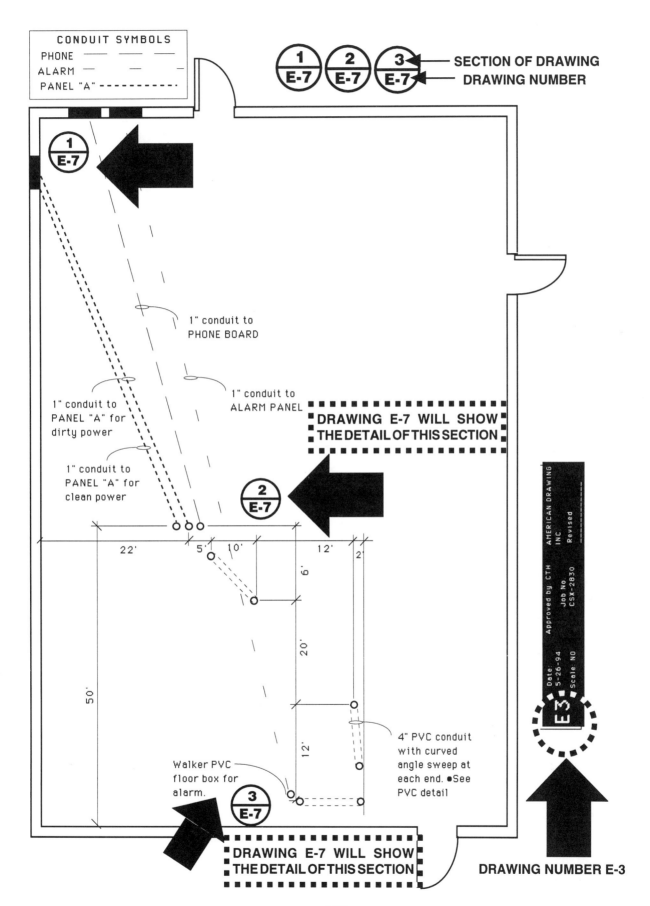

CONDUIT SYMBOLS
PHONE ————— ————
ALARM — — — —
PANEL "A" - - - - - - - - -

SECTION OF DRAWING
DRAWING NUMBER

1" conduit to
PHONE BOARD

1" conduit to
ALARM PANEL

1" conduit to
PANEL "A" for
dirty power

1" conduit to
PANEL "A" for
clean power

DRAWING E-7 WILL SHOW
THE DETAIL OF THIS SECTION

22'   5'   10'   12'   2'

6'

20'

50'

12'

Walker PVC
floor box for
alarm.

4" PVC conduit
with curved
angle sweep at
each end. ●See
PVC detail

Date: 5-26-94   Approved by: CTH   AMERICAN DRAWING
Scale: NO   Job No.   INC.
                  CSX-2830   Revised

E-3

DRAWING E-7 WILL SHOW
THE DETAIL OF THIS SECTION

DRAWING NUMBER E-3

103

DETAIL DRAWINGS

Drawing E-7 shows details from drawing E-3.

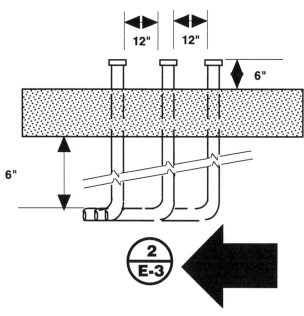

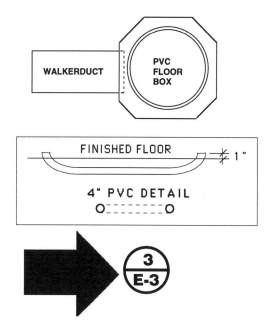

This detail is of SECTION 2
on DRAWING E-3

This detail is of SECTION 3
on DRAWING E-3

DRAWING NUMBER E-7

E7	Date: 5-26-94	Approved by: CTH	AMERICAN DRAWING INC.
	Scale: NO	Job No. CSX-2830	Revised

LIGHTING PLAN

The lighting plan shows the layout of the fixtures and the dimensions they are to be installed.

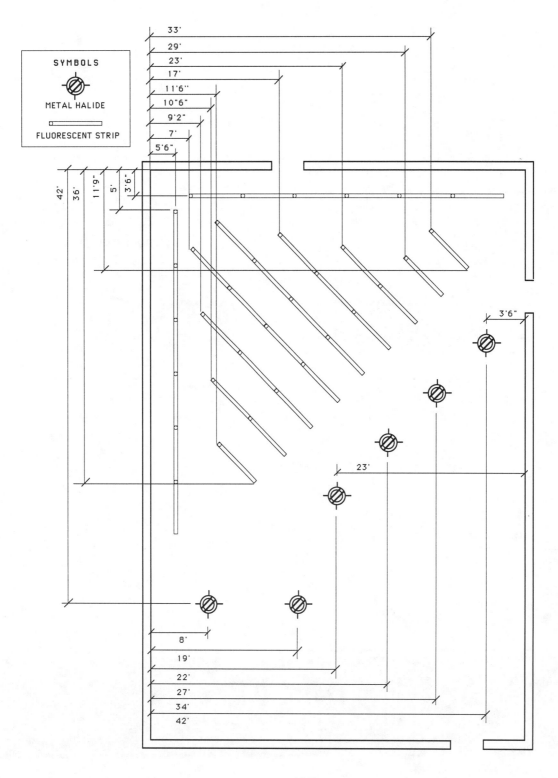

SPECIFICATIONS

Specifications for a construction project is the written description of what is required by the owner, engineer, and architect. Specifications give the grade of materials and the manner in which they are to be installed. Electricians don't always have access to the specifications. In this case they follow the schedule which will list the type of equipment to be installed, including notes.

1. Work Included:

A. Conduit, Wires and Cable
B. Boxes and Wiring devices
C. Safety Switches
D. Service Entrance and Utility Coordination
E. Data Cable (Material furnished by Owner)
F. Conduit for Thermostats (Wiring by Mechanical Contractor)
G. Conduit for Telephone System
H. Conduit for Security System
I. Field Testing
J. Utility Company fees and charges for service to the project, including setting the meters
•Note: Refundable deposits for permanent service will be paid by the owner.

2. Quality Requirements:

A. Provide UL approved materials and devices
B. Comply with NFPA 70 National Electrical Code as minimum standards and local Codes

3. Conduit:

A. Rigid: Galvanized steel with threaded couplings. Intermediate grade may be used instead of rigid where permitted by the Code.
B. Thin Wall (EMT): Galvanized steel with liquid tight compression type fittings in concrete slabs and set screw fittings in dry locations.
C. Nonmetallic: Rigid PVC, Schedule 40, with factory made bends, joints solvent welded.
D. Flexible Conduit: Spirally wound interlocked steel armored raceway conforming to NEC 350 and UL.

4. Wires and Cables:

A. Soft drawn copper of not less than 98% conductivity.
B. Sizes #8 and larger shall be stranded.
C. Minimum size wire permitted #12. Use #10 if circuit exceeds 100 feet and #8 where noted.
D. Use 600v THW insulation on building and branch circuit wiring unless otherwise indicated on the drawings. THHN insulation may be used in dry locations only.
E. Data cable size #24 AWG, 3 pair, provided by owner upon notice by contractor of required delivery date.

5. Outlet, Switch, Junction and Pull Boxes:

A. Boxes:	Galvanized steel conforming to NEC and UL Requirements
B. Exterior Boxes:	Weatherproof type threaded hubs and gasket covers

6. Wiring Devices:

A. Wall Switches:	Specification grade, quiet slow make-slow break design, toggle handle, rated 15 amps, 120v, color brown
B. Standard Receptacles:	Specification grade, full gang size, polarized duplex, parallel blade, U-grounding slot, rated 20 amps, 120v, color brown
C. Device Plates:	General use, Bakelite with smooth finish and rolled outer edges, color brown
D. Safety Switches:	General Duty, fusible type with NEMA Type 1 enclosure indoors, and type 3R enclosure outdoors

6. Conduit Installation:

A. Use rigid conduit in earth and where exposed to weather. Make joints with standard thread couplings or unions. Protect newly cut conduit threads with graphite grease or other rust resistive, non-insulating compound. Use double locknuts at terminations.

B. Use EMT only in dry, protected areas where not subject to mechanical damage.

C. PVC conduit may be used for underground feeders from service entrance to panels, to site lighting, and to pylon/billboard signs only. Use rigid steel, long radius elbows on risers from underground conduit. Provide "THW" copper grounding conductors for entire length of nonmetallic conduit and connect to rigid steel.

D. Provide moisture seal where conduits penetrate outside walls or slabs-on-grade.

E. Secure conduits to building structure at intervals of not more than 5 feet for sizes up to and including, 2 inch; and at intervals not to exceed 8 feet for larger sizes.

F. Support conduit in concrete slab construction at every 5 feet or less and secure with #12 AWG wire.

G. Run conduits concealed. Exposed runs, where approved by the architect, shall be installed in neat, symmetrical lines parallel to, or at right angles to, building lines. Tight to metal deck.

H. Install conduit 6 inch minimum from hot water lines.

I. Terminate conduit at equipment subject to vibration with flexible connections. In wet locations, use Neoprene or Polychloroprene covered flex with water tight fittings. Provide for continuity of ground.

J. Provide conduit system for mechanical control wiring.

K. Provide conduit system from telephone system from terminal panelboard to counter location, as noted on plans.

L. Provide conduit for telephone service entrance. Entrance shall be underground from telephone equipment pedestal, and run to phone equipment board.

7. Conductor Installation:

A.   Maintain color coding throughout the electric system.
B.   Where the distance between the panelboard and the first outlet in a branch circuit is more than 60 feet, use #10 AWG wire or larger.
C.   Make conductor length for parallel feeders identical.
D.   Provide solderless connections only.

8. Outlet, Switch and Junction Box Installation:

A.   Install flush type boxes slightly recessed to allow full perimeter contact of device plates.
B.   Install boxes for convenience outlets 12 inches above floor, unless otherwise indicated on the drawings.
C.   Install switch boxes 4' 6" above the floor, unless otherwise indicated on the drawings.
D.   In masonry construction, the height of boxes may be adjusted slightly to fit coursing.
E.   Set boxes for floor outlets flush to floor, unless otherwise indicated on the drawings.
F.   "J" Boxes are to be concealed behind the sheet rock.

9. Wiring Device Installation:

A.   Place wall switches on strike side of doors unless otherwise indicated on the drawings.
B.   Install device plates with perimeter edges in full contact with finish surfaces.

10. Field Testing:

A.   Test all circuits with a "Multi" Tester to determine that the system is free of short circuits and that the phase conductors are not grounded.
B.   Check motor controllers for proper operation.
C.   Check electrical equipment for proper operation.
D.   Immediately replace defective or damaged materials and equipment.

11. Data Cable Installation:

A.   Cable shall be supplied by owner and received by contractor.
B.   Cable lines shall be run straight and parallel, tied together with nonconductive material.
C.   Provide 6 feet of extra cable length at each equipment location.
D.   Tag each end of Data Cable for each circuit.

OVERHEAD ELECTRICAL SERVICE

1. Components:

A. Conductors:	As required by local utility.
B. Service Rack:	Three (3) or four (4) wire racks, as determined by local utility for specified service.
C. Service Weatherhead:	Cast metal conforming to local utility weatherhead requirements.
D. Service Mast:	Rigid Tubular Metal Fabrication with provisions for attachment of service rack and weatherhead.
E. Meter Socket:	Conform to local utility requirements.
F. Conduit:	Rigid metal conduit complete with watertight fittings.

2. Installation:

A.   Install service rack and weatherhead at proper height. Provide mast kit, if required.

B.   Extend mast head to provide a minimum ground clearance of 20 feet when overhead service is near dumpster location.

C.   Install rigid conduit to weather proof meter socket.

D.   Provide terminations, coordinate with local utility company.

3. Panelboards:

A.   Metal cabinets with gray enamel finish complete with panel trim having concealed hinges and flush lock, concealed trip clamps and screw cover front; Galvanized steel back with knockouts. Provide two keys for each panel.

B.   Factory assembled, three (3) phase - four (4) Wire; and Single Phase - three (3) wire. Full capacity, solid neutral, with sequence style bussing.

4. Circuit Breakers:

A.   Molded case, automatic air circuit breakers as supplied with thermal and magnet trip and trip-free position separate from either "ON" or "OFF" positions; interrupting rating of 10,000 AIC.

B.   Provide switching duty circuit breakers for branch circuits.

5. Identification of Panels:

A.   Provide a laminated plastic plate at the top of panel engraved with designation identical on panelboard schedule or riser diagram. Identify each overcurrent device with a laminated plastic plate engraved with a description of item protected.

B.   Provide a typewritten directory to the inside cover indicating loads controlled by each circuit, identical to panel schedules.

LIGHTING

A. Products: Refer to lighting fixture schedule on drawing for types. Provide necessary trim, brackets, and accessories for complete installation. No substitutes will be accepted, unless Architect considers to be equal to what was specified.

B. Lamps: First line quality.

C. Ballasts: Fluorescent - UL listed, Type "P" with automatic resetting thermal protection, rapid start. Metal Halide - UL listed, Type CWA, peak load automatic transformer.

D. Time Clocks: 24 hour dial with two (2) trippers.

E. Control Relay: Six to twelve poles, as required provide additional relays, if required to accommodate site lighting. Balance load between relays.

F. Building: Support light fixtures from structure only. Provide gaskets or necessary accessories to prevent light leaks around trim. Install fixtures in a manner to properly dissipate generated heat. Equip each fixture with owner furnished lamps, as scheduled.

G. Site Installation: Set poles plumb, rigidly in place in accordance with manufacturer's recommendations. Provide necessary brackets, caps and accessories, factory energized light and sign circuits and set time (Dusk). Time clock shall deenergize light and sign circuits at set time (12:00 A.M.) to turn lights off.

Provide necessary exit and emergency egress lighting, clarifying the exit lights will be illuminated to a minimum of five footcandles, and egress lighting will provide not less than one footcandle at the most remote lighted area. For the means of egress.

110

WIRING DEVICES

STANDARD RECEPTACLE CONFIGURATIONS

NEMA ANSI	Receptacle Configuration	Rating	
5-15 C73.11		15A 125V	**2 POLE 3 WIRE**
5-20 C73.12		20A 125V	
5-30 C73.45		30A 125V	
5-50 C73.46		50A 125V	
6-15 C73.20		15A 250V	
6-20 C73.51		20A 250V	
6-30 C73.52		30A 250V	
6-50 C73.53		50A 250V	
7-15 C73.28		15A 277V	
7-20 C73.63		20A 277V	
7-30 C73.64		30A 277V	
7-50 C73.65		50A 277V	
10-20 C73.23		20A 125/250V	**3 POLE 3 WIRE**
10-30 C73.24		30A 125/250V	
10-50 C73.25		50A 125/250V	
11-15 C73.54		15A 3φ 250V	
11-20 C73.55		20A 3φ 250V	

Rating	Receptacle Configuration	NEMA ANSI	
30A 3φ 250V		11-30 C73.56	**3P3W**
50A 3φ 250V		11-50 C73.57	
15A 125/250V		14-15 C73.49	**3 POLE 4 WIRE**
20A 125/250V		14-20 C73.50	
30A 125/250V		14-30 C73.16	
50A 125/250V		14-50 C73.17	
60A 125/250V		14-60 C73.18	
15A 3φ 250V		15-15 C73.58	
20A 3φ 250V		15-20 C73.59	
30A 3φ 250V		15-30 C73.60	
50A 3φ 250V		15-50 C73.61	
60A 3φ 250V		15-60 C73.62	
15A 3φY 120/208V		18-15 C73.15	**4 POLE 4 WIRE**
20A 3φY 120/208V		18-20 C73.26	
30A 3φY 120/208V		18-30 C73.47	
50A 3φY 120/208V		18-50 C73.48	
60A 3φY 120/208V		18-60 C73.27	

111

WIRING DEVICES

STANDARD RECEPTACLE CONFIGURATIONS

NEMA / ANSI	Receptacle Configuration	Rating	
ML2 / C73.44		15A 125V	2 POLE 3 WIRE
L5-15 / C73.42		15A 125V	
L5-20 / C73.72		20A 125V	
L5-30 / C73.73		30A 125V	
L6-15 / C73.74		15A 250V	
L6-20 / C73.75		20A 250V	
L6-30 / C73.76		30A 250V	
L7-15 / C73.43		15A 277V	
L7-20 / C73.77		20A 277V	
L7-30 / C73.78		30A 277V	
L8-20 / C73.79		20A 480V	
L8-30 / C73.80		30A 480V	
L9-20 / C73.81		20A 600V	
L9-30 / C73.82		30A 600V	
ML3 / C73.30		15A 125/250V	3 POLE 3 WIRE
L10-20 / C73.96		20A 125/250V	
L10-30 / C73.97		30A 125/250V	
L11-15 / C73.98		15A 3φ 250V	
L11-20 / C73.99		20A 3φ 250V	
L11-30 / C73-100		30A 3φ 250V	
L12-20 / C73.101		20A 3φ 480V	

	Rating	Configuration	NEMA / ANSI
3P3W	30A 3φ 480V		L12-30 / C73.102
	30A 3φ 600V		L13-30 / C73.103
3 POLE 4 WIRE	20A 125/250V		L14-20 / C73.83
	30A 125/250V		L14-30 / C73.84
	20A 3φ 250V		L15-20 / C73.85
	30A 3φ 250V		L15-30 / C73.86
	20A 3φ 480V		L16-20 / C73.87
	30A 3φ 480V		L16-30 / C73.88
	30A 3φ 600V		L17-30 / C73.89
4 POLE 4 WIRE	20A 3φY 120/208V		L18-20 / C73.104
	30A 3φY 120/208V		L18-30 / C73.105
	20A 3φY 277/480V		L19-20 / C73.106
	30A 3φY 277/480V		L19-30 / C73.107
	20A 3φY 347/600V		L20-20 / C73.108
	30A 3φY 347/600V		L20-30 / C73.109
4 POLE 5 WIRE	20A 3φY 120/208V		L21-20 / C73.90
	30A 3φY 120/208V		L21-30 / C73.91
	20A 3φY 277/480V		L22-20 / C73.92
	30A 3φY 277/480V		L22-30 / C73.93
	20A 3φY 347/600V		L23-20 / C73.94
	30A 3φY 347/600V		L23-30 / C73.95

MATERIAL DESIGNATIONS

EARTH / COMPACTED

POROUS FILL
(STONE OR GRAVEL, ETC.)

ROCK

CONCRETE / LIGHTWEIGHT
(CONCRETE FILL)

CONCRETE / STRUCTURAL
(CAST-IN-PLACE, PRECAST)

BRICK / COMMON

BRICK / FACE

CONCRETE MASONRY UNITS
(SMALL SCALE)

CONCRETE MASONRY UNITS
(LARGE SCALE)

CAST STONE CONCRETE

STONE / CUT

MARBLE

STONE / RUBBLE

CLAY TILE / STRUCTURAL

CLAY TILE / UNGLAZED

CLAY TILE / GLAZED

METAL
(SMALL SCALE)

PLYWOOD
(LARGE SCALE)

PLYWOOD
(SMALL SCALE)

WOOD / FINISH

WOOD / ROUGH

WOOD / BLOCKING

INSULATION / LOOSE
OR BATT

INSULATION / RIGID

GLASS
(LARGE SCALE)

GLASS
(SMALL SCALE)

ACOUSTICAL TILE

CERAMIC TILE

GYPSUM WALL BOARD

PLASTER, SAND, CEMENT,
GROUT

RESILIENT FLOORING

TERRAZZO

ELEVATION

CONCRETE, PLASTER, STUCCO
(AS INDICATED)

CONCRETE MASONRY UNITS

GLAZING

BRICK

PARTITION CONSTRUCTION PLAN

 WOOD STUCCO

 STEEL STUD

 CMU

CMU W/FILLED CELLS

113

EXAMS

(1) Using your ruler, approximately how far from the west wall would you install the outlet box for the ceiling fan? _____

(2) How far apart (on center) are the recessed lights over the sink area? _____

(3) How far from the north wall is the outlet box for the ceiling light? _____

(4) The outdoor wall-mounted lights are how far apart (on center)? _____

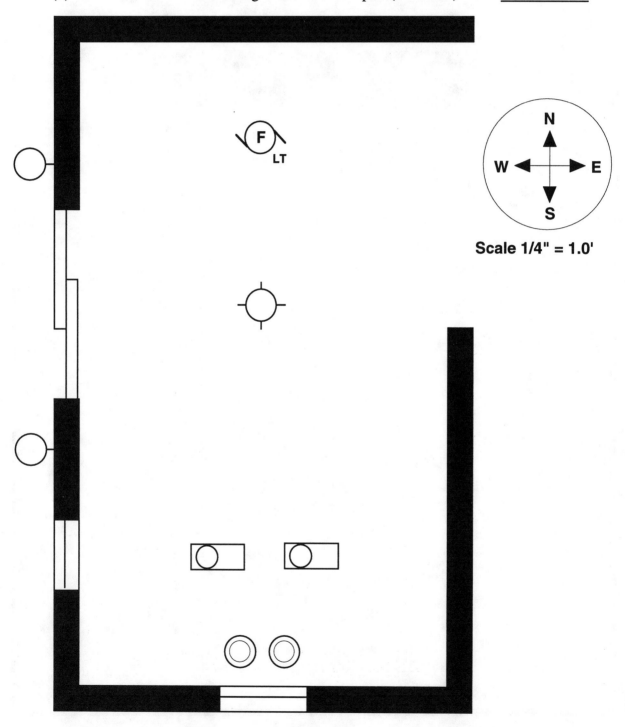

Scale 1/4" = 1.0'

1. The three electrical diagrams most frequently used?

(a) schematic, pictorial, blueprints   **(b) blueprints, site plan, detail plan**
(c) riser plan, elevation detail, site plan   **(d) pictorial, site plan, schematic**

2. Blueprints _____.

(a) contain many different types of drawings
(b) are viewed from the top view
(c) will contain the schedules
(d) all of the above

3. Which direction is North on a blueprint?

(a) top (b) bottom (c) right (d) left

4. How would the clearance necessary for overhead service lines be determined?

(a) by examining the plans
(b) by the height of the roof above grade
(c) by approval of the local utility company
(d) by citing pertinent NEC sections to the contractor

5. Switches installed out of sight from the light fixture should _____.

(a) be 3-way (b) be on a time-clock (c) have a pilot light (d) be locked

6. The drawing shown below is called a _____ .

(a) schematic drawing (b) detail drawing (c) riser drawing (d) one-line drawing

1. A drawing indicates a solid line with "CO" inserted periodically, what does this represent?

(a) a pipe with a clean-out fitting
(b) a pipe for carbon monoxide
(c) a length of empty conduit
(d) all of the above

2. Which of the following does not show actual wiring?

(a) one-line diagram   (b) schematic diagram   (c) floor plan   (d) pictorial

3. On large jobs, where several electricians are working from the same set of plans, it is helpful ____.

(a) to have daily meetings with each crew and have them explain the work completed
(b) to have only one electrician read the plans on each crew
(c) for each electrician to keep track of the circuits completed by drawing a squiggly red line through the work completed
(d) to mark each box when wiring is completed and notify the lead

4. The letters I.G. on the drawing would indicate ____.

(a) internal ground   (b) isolated ground   (c) intentional ground   (d) amperage gauge

5. How are the number of conductors indicated in a circuit-symbol?

(a) with a number written across the circuit line
(b) by the number of lines drawn across the circuit line
(c) by a number at the arrow
(d) all of the above

6. The letters MTR on the drawing would indicate ____.

(a) middle of run   (b) manufacture   (c) motor   (d) motor-tie-resistor

1. On which side of the door should switches be located?

(a) hinged side   (b) opposite of hinged side   (c) back side   (d) door jam vertical

2. A dot on a wire indicates _____.

(a) a soldered joint   (b) an electrical connection   (c) a fused joint   (d) a wire nut

3. If the scale is 1/4" = 1' and the conduit run is 2 3/4" on the drawing, the length of the conduit run is _____.

(a) 11'   (b) 2' 9"   (c) 16' 9"   (d) 13'

4. The letters P.O.S. on the drawing would indicate _____.

(a) pull-switch   (b) positive stop   (c) position on switch   (d) point of sale

5. The best location for a panelboard is _____.

(a) garage   (b) furnace room   (c) basement   (d) nearest to heavy loads

6. The drawing shown below is a _____.

(a) building plan   (b) site plan   (c) elevation plan   (d) riser plan

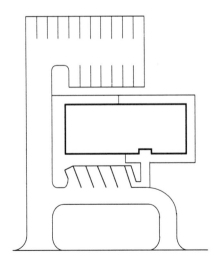

EXAM #5

1. The letters XFMR on the drawing would indicate ____.

(a) oil-resistant insulation   (b) center of furnace room   (c) transformer   (d) impedance

2. Why is it necessary for an electrician to be concerned with the type and thickness of wall finish material?

(a) to determine the lighting level required
(b) to determine the length of the wires
(c) to set the mounting depth of boxes
(d) none of the above

3. The symbol for a switch is a ____.

(a) circle with S   (b) square with S   (c) capital S   (d) circle with SW

4. The two kinds of blueprints you will use on the job are ____.

(a) floor plan and one-line diagram   (b) schematic and pictorial
(c) detail and riser plans   (d) one-line diagram and schematic

5. The letters PNL on the drawing would indicate ___.

(a) pilot-neutral light   (b) panel   (c) positive-negative-lag   (d) pilot night light

6. The drawing shown below is called a ____.

(a) riser diagram   (b) power schedule   (c) utility plan   (d) slab detail

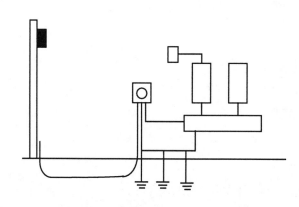

119

EXAM #6

1. What does the symbol S_p indicate?

(a) single-pole   (b) safety-pull   (c) switch with pilot   (d) sump pump

2. A complete electrical circuit is shown by a ____.

(a) schematic   (b) one-line diagram   (c) floor plan   (d) working drawing

3. NTS means ____.

(a) National Technical Society   (b) Northern Temperature Standard
(c) Not To Scale   (d) Night Timer Safety

4. A drawing that illustrates components and wiring like a photograph is referred to as a _____.

(a) schematic   (b) detail drawing   (c) one-line drawing   (d) pictorial drawing

5. Generally, electricians do their wiring from a ____.

(a) floor plan   (b) pictorial drawing   (c) schematic diagram   (d) riser plan

6. Using a ruler the approximate inside dimensions of the garage would be ____ by ____.

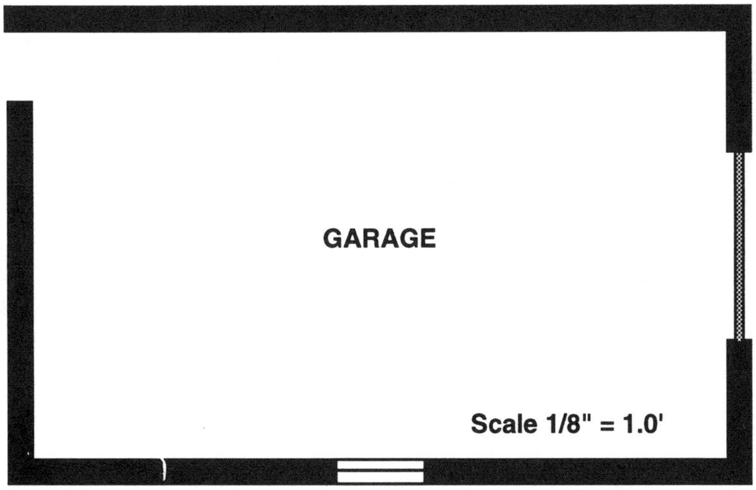

GARAGE

Scale 1/8" = 1.0'

1. The letters U.O.N. on the drawing would indicate ____.

(a) unbalance on neutral   (b) under open neutral
(c) unless otherwise noted   (d) under other neutral

2. A switched duplex receptacle is indicated on the drawing by _____.

(a) an SR inside a circle   (b) an S beside two lines
(c) a circle, half shaded, and two lines   (d) an SR inside a circle with two lines

3. When working from an electrical drawing, you should start from the ____.

(a) lower right-hand corner   (b) center
(c) upper left-hand corner   (d) bottom

4. When tracing a branch circuit from a drawing start at the ____.

(a) switch location   (b) panelboard   (c) receptacle   (d) left-hand corner

5. The letters AIC on the drawing would indicate ____.

(a) alternating isolated current   (b) amperes interrupting capacity
(c) amperes isolated continuous   (d) automatic interrupted current

6. The letters HACR on the drawing would indicate ____.

(a) high alternating current resistive   (b) holding auto-control remote
(c) heating-air conditioning-refrigeration (d) heavy arc control relay

1. How many telephones are shown?

(a) 1 (b) 2 (c) 3 (d) 4

2. How many duplex receptacles are shown?

(a) 12 (b) 13 (c) 14 (d) 15

3. Which circuit has lights and a receptacle?

(a) A-14 (b) B-8, 10,12 (c) A-19 (d) A-11

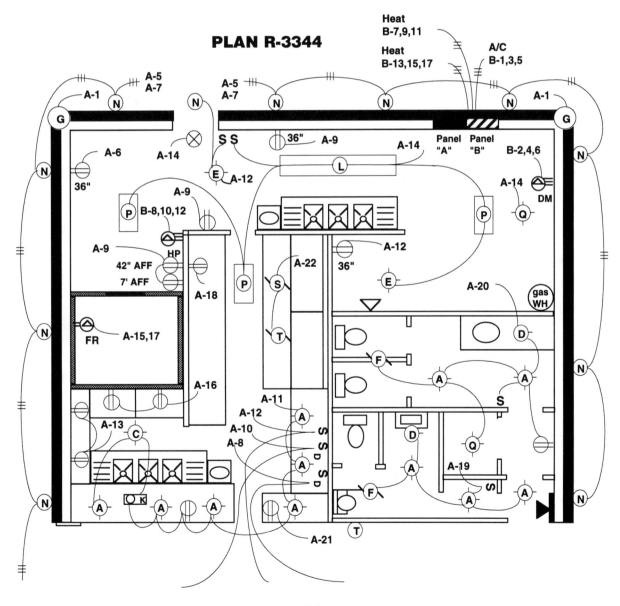

PLAN R-3344

1. The number of exit lights shown on the drawing "Part B" is ____.

(a) 1   (b) 2   (c) 3   (d) 4

2. The number of interior wall mounted light fixtures on drawing "Part B" is ____.

(a) 22   (b) 18   (c) 15   (d) 30

PART "B" OF PLAN R-3344

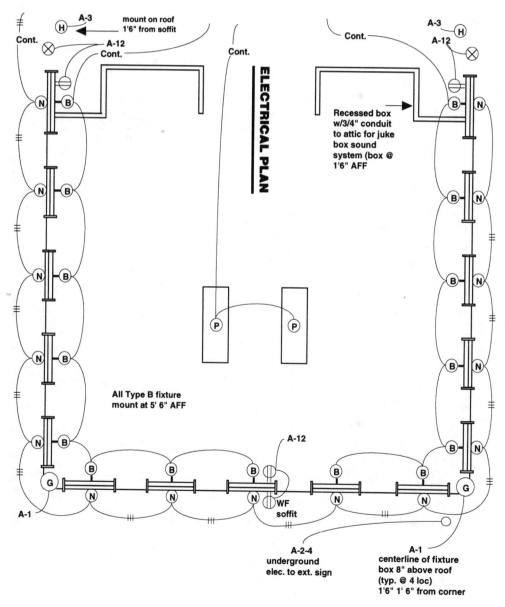

•Questions on this exam are from the plans of the restaurant **R-3344** including schedules.

1. Circuit A-11 has _____ lights.

(a) 7   (b) 8   (c) 9   (d) 6

2. How many "Q" light fixtures are shown?

(a) 1   (b) 2   (c) 3   (d) 4

3. Circuit A-21 supplys the _____.

(a) work lights   (b) dough mixer   (c) cash register   (d) fans

4. How many 3-way switches are shown?

(a) 0   (b) 1   (c) 2   (d) 4

5. How many "N" light fixtures are shown?

(a) 23   (b) 24   (c) 25   (d) 26

6. How many flourescent fixtures are shown?

(a) 7   (b) 6   (c) 5   (d) 4

7. Circuit A-19 supplies _____ lights.

(a) 5   (b) 4   (c) 3   (d) 2

8. How many lights are connected to circuit A-12?

(a) 2   (b) 3   (c) 5   (d) 6

•Questions on this exam are from the plans of the restaurant **R-3344** including schedules.

1. (T) is the symbol for ____.

(a) timer   (b) thermostat   (c) fan   (d) clock

2. Circuit A-20 supplies ____ receptacle(s).

(a) 1   (b) 2   (c) 3   (d) 4

3. How many duplex receptacles are connected to circuit A-12?

(a) 0   (b) 2   (c) 4   (d) 5

4. Circuit A-1 supplies ____ light(s).

(a) 4   (b) 3   (c) 2   (d) 1

5. How many special receptacles are shown on drawing R-3344?

(a) 4   (b) 3   (c) 2   (d) 1

6. Circuit A-14 supplies ____ lights.

(a) 5   (b) 6   (c) 7   (d) 8

7. How many 3-pole breakers are required?

(a) 5   (b) 4   (c) 3   (d) 15

8. Circuit A-9 supplies ____ receptacle(s).

(a) 4   (b) 3   (c) 2   (d) 1

1. A pictorial drawing would show ____.

(a) the perspective view   (b) the site plan   (c) the detail   (d) the cross section

2. The drawing shown below would be a ____.

(a) one-line diagram   (b) schematic diagram   (c) main diagram   (d) riser diagram

3. is the material designation for ____.

(a) wood/finish   (b) wood/rough   (c) brick face   (d) ceramic tile

4. If the scale is 1/8" = 1' and the conduit run measures 5 3/4" on the drawing, how many lengths of 10' conduit is needed?

(a) 3   (b) 4   (c) 5   (d) 6

5. is the symbol for ____.

(a) conduit turned up   (b) conduit turned down
(c) homerun down   (d) wiring turned down

6. is the material designation for ____.

(a) rock   (b) concrete/structural   (c) cast stone concrete   (d) porous fill (gravel)

EXAM #13

•*Fill in the blank with the correct letter from choices below for the symbol*

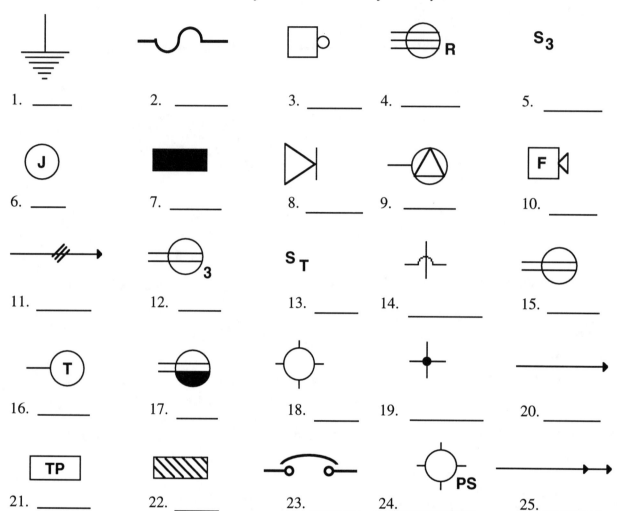

1. _____   2. _____   3. _____   4. _____   5. _____

6. _____   7. _____   8. _____   9. _____   10. _____

11. _____   12. _____   13. _____   14. _____   15. _____

16. _____   17. _____   18. _____   19. _____   20. _____

21. _____   22. _____   23. _____   24. _____   25. _____

• *Choose a letter ( ) and fill in the blank above:*

(A) power panel
(B) fusible element
(C) two branch circuit home runs to panel
(D) time switch
(E) ceiling outlet
(F) duplex outlet, split circuit
(G) circuit breaker
(H) telephone
(I) thermostat
(J) fire alarm bell
(K) single special-purpose receptacle
(L) fire alarm horn
(M) wiring connected

(N) triplex receptacle outlet
(O) single branch circuit home run to panel
(P) wiring crossed not connected
(Q) lampholder with pull switch
(R) transformer pad
(S) junction box
(T) ground
(U) range receptacle
(W) switch 3-way
(X) duplex receptacle
(Y) branch circuit lighting panel
(Z) single branch circuit home run to panel (3-wire)

127

EXAM #14

•*Fill in the blank with the correct letter from choices below for the symbol*

S_K   (SD)   ⊖ WP   (F)   (S)

1. ____   2. ____   3. ____   4. ____   5. ____

S_P   ⊗   [D]   (M)   ☐

6. ____   7. ____   8. ____   9. ____   10. ____

[●]   S_F   ├─┼─┼─┤   ☐   (H)

11. ____   12. ____   13. ____   14. ____   15. ____

⊠   (R)   [○─]   (B)   [F]○

16. ____   17. ____   18. ____   19. ____   20. ____

────○   ⊖ GR   ◣   ────●

21. ____   22. ____   23. ____   24. ____

• *Choose a letter ( ) and fill in the blank above:*

(A) exit light	(M) fixture recessed
(B) motor	(N) weatherproof outlet
(C) bare-lamp fluorescent strip	(O) ceiling pull switch
(D) motor starter	(P) blanked outlet
(E) electric door opener	(Q) grounded duplex receptacle
(F) switch fused	(R) wiring turned down
(G) fan outlet	(S) switch with pilot
(H) push button	(T) fluorescent fixture
(I) fire alarm bell	(U) heating panel
(J) buzzer	(W) switch key operated
(K) smoke detector	(X) humidistat
(L) safety switch	(Y) wiring turned up

ANSWERS

EXAM #1

1. 8 feet
2. 2 feet
3. 11 feet
4. 12 feet

EXAM #2

1. (a) schematic, pictorial, blueprints
2. (d) all of the above
3. (a) top
4. (a) by examining plans
5. (c) have a pilot light
6. (b) detail drawing

EXAM #3

1. (a) a pipe with a clean-out fitting
2. (c) floor plan
3. (c) draw squiggly red line
4. (b) isolated ground
5. (b) by the number of lines drawn across the circuit line
6. (c) motor

EXAM #4

1. (b) opposite of hinged side
2. (b) an electrical connection
3. (a) 11'
4. (d) point of sale
5. (d) nearest to heavy loads
6. (b) site plan

EXAM #5

1. (c) transformer
2. (c) to set the mounting depth of boxes
3. (c) capital S
4. (a) floor plan and one-line diagram
5. (b) panel
6. (a) riser diagram

EXAM #6

1. (c) switch with pilot
2. (a) schematic
3. (c) Not To Scale
4. (d) pictorial drawing
5. (a) floor plan
6. 18' x 30'

EXAM #7

1. (c) unless otherwise noted
2. (c) a circle, half shaded, and two lines
3. (c) upper left-hand corner
4. (b) panelboard
5. (b) amperes interrupting capacity
6. (c) heating-air conditioning-refrigeration

EXAM #8

1. (b) two
2. (c) fourteen
3. (d) A-11

EXAM #9

1. (b) two
2. (c) fifteen

EXAM #10

1. (b) eight
2. (b) two
3. (c) cash register •See panel schedule
4. (a) zero
5. (d) twenty-six
6. (a) seven
7. (b) four
8. (d) six

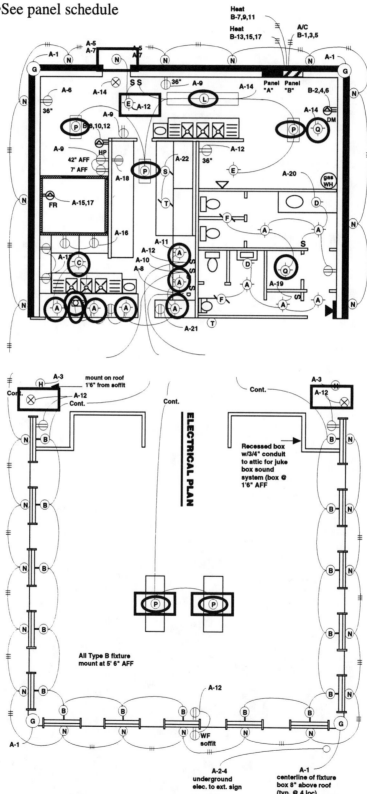

EXAM #11

1. (b) thermostat
2. (a) one
3. (d) five
4. (a) four
5. (b) three
6. (c) seven
7. (a) five •See panel schedule
8. (a) four

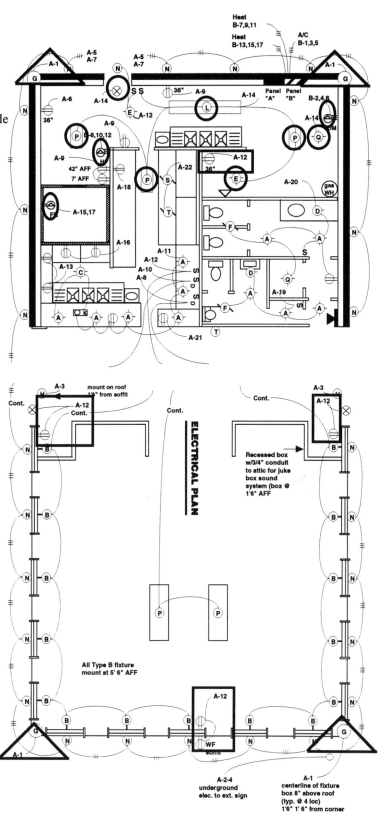

EXAM #12

1. (a) the perspective view
2. (b) schematic diagram
3. (d) ceramic tile
4. (c) five
5. (a) conduit turned up
6. (d) porous fill (gravel)

EXAM #13

1. (T)
2. (B)
3. (J)
4. (U)
5. (W)
6. (S)
7. (Y)
8. (H)
9. (K)
10. (L)
11. (Z)
12. (N)
13. (D)
14. (P)
15. (X)
16. (I)
17. (F)
18. (E)
19. (M)
20. (O)
21. (R)
22. (A)
23. (G)
24. (Q)
25. (C)

EXAM #14

1. (W)
2. (K)
3. (N)
4. (G)
5. (O)
6. (S)
7. (A)
8. (E)
9. (B)
10. (J)
11. (H)
12. (F)
13. (C)
14. (L)
15. (X)
16. (D)
17. (M)
18. (T)
19. (P)
20. (I)
21. (Y)
22. (Q)
23. (U)
24. (R)

VIDEOS
By Tom Henry

12 BRAND NEW VIDEOS FOR ELECTRICAL EXAM PREPARATION!

12 VIDEO TAPES EXPLAINING EXAM CALCULATIONS- ALL TAPES ARE APPROXIMATELY 75-90 MINUTES

THE EXAM
Video #301

OHMS LAW - THEORY
Video #302

VOLTAGE DROP - RESISTANCE
Video #303

AMPACITY CORRECTION FACTORS
Video #304

MOTORS
Video #305

COOKING EQUIPMENT DEMAND FACTORS
Video #306

DWELLING-RESIDENTIAL SERVICE SIZING
Video #307

BOX and CONDUIT SIZING
Video #308

SINGLE-PHASE TRANSFORMERS
Video #309

THREE-PHASE TRANSFORMERS
Video #310

COMMERCIAL-MULTIFAMILY SERVICE SIZING
Video #311

MOTOR CONTROL - SWITCH CONNECTIONS
Video #312

EACH VIDEO $29.95
JOURNEYMAN SERIES $250.00
ITEM # 313 (Includes tapes #301 through #309 total of 9 videos- SAVE $$$$)

MASTER SERIES $350.00
ITEM # 314 (All 12 video tapes- SAVE $$$$)

AUDIOS
By Tom Henry

3 AUDIO TAPES FOR ELECTRICAL EXAM PREPARATION!

The troublesome CLOSED BOOK is now made easy as Tom Henry goes over each answer in DETAIL on audio tape. 3 CLOSED BOOK exams with **150** questions selected by Tom Henry to help the exam applicant learn this part of the electrical examination. Each CLOSED BOOK EXAM contains 50 questions. A ONE HOUR tape narrated by Tom Henry gives in full detail the answer to each question on each exam. A total of 3 hours of audio! You will learn how to memorize and store items in your mind. These exams can be worked over and over again. **The 3 audio tapes can be listened to as you drive in your truck or as you sit at home.** The student will memorize burial depths, definitions, service clearance heights, etc.With **ITEM #192** you will receive a workbook containing 3 closed book exams plus 3 audio tapes by *Tom Henry.* Price $29.00

 Call 1-800-642-2633 Today!

...Start your complete electrical library with *Tom Henry* Publications!!!

Book #101 - An ideal book for an electrician needing a refresher on Ohm's Law. Explains AC and DC in layman terms with easier to understand formulas, sketches of circuits, series & parallel circuits, Exact K for voltage drop calculations, function of neutral, review on math for the electrician! Contains over 100 Questions & Answers.

Book #102 - Based on the 1993 Code! An excellent study-aid for the helper, apprentice, or electrician to prepare for the Journeyman license exam. The book contains **10** closed book exams and **12** open book exams. Over **1100** actual exam questions with answers and Code references. An excellent book to study the Code!!

Book #103 - Based on the 1993 Code! A book designed to advance the electrician in the Code book from the Journeyman level. Contains **8** closed book exams and **10** open book exams. Over **1100** actual exam questions with answers and Code references. An excellent study-aid, takes you cover to cover in the Code including exceptions and Fine Print Notes!!

Book #104- Finally a book written by an electrician in an easy to study format to prepare the everyday electrician in this difficult area of the exam. Single-phase, three-phase, delta-wye, load balancing, neutral calculations, open-delta, high-leg delta, etc. Over 100 calculations with answers!!

Book #105 - Based on the 1993 Code! Tom Henry's TOP SELLER!! Everything on calculations- **8** chapters - Cooking equipment demands, single-phase ranges on a 3 phase system, ampacity, box-conduit fill, motor circuits, service sizing, feeder sizing, cable tray calculations, and mobile homes, etc. A must!

Book #110 - Tom Henry's favorite reference book. A complete reference book for the electrician that gives the definitions of the language used in the construction field. Also contains formulas used for the exam and in the field, diagrams showing motor, transformer, and switch connections, etc...

Book #115 - The Electrical Alarm Contractor Exam Workbook designed to prepare you for the burglar and fire alarm exam. Hundreds of exam questions with answers. OSHA, UL, NFPA, Life Safety Code, Business Law, loop circuits, etc. !!!!!!

Book #171 - Tom Henry's quiz book! 60 quizzes on tool identification, wiring methods, blueprint symbols, meter reading, circuit testing, controls, proper installation, etc. This book was written to help prepare an electrician for the mechanical, comprehension and aptitude testing of the exam.

Book #197 - Based on the 1993 Code! The Grounding Workbook designed for training programs to take the mystery out of grounding. Tom Henry's favorite book! Every person in the electrical industry should work the 27 exams this book contains.
Book #199 - INSTRUCTORS GUIDE

Book #198 - Based on the 1993 Code! The Pictorial Workbook of the Code - Volume One. The Code book in pictures. Volume One starts at the beginning: Articles 90, 100, 110, 200, 210 & 215. A must book for every electrical training program! Now you can "learn" the Code!
Book #201 - INSTRUCTORS GUIDE

Book #108 - KEY WORD INDEX. Every word in the 1993 Code book put into an index with page numbers. Now you can find it in the Code in **seconds**! This is the book the electricians are raving about. Don't be without one!

Book #236 - Based on the 1993 Code! The Pictorial Workbook of the Code - Volume Two. Volume Two starts at Calculations Article 220. This Volume also includes Outdoor Circuits Article 225, Services Article 230 and Overcurrent Protection Article 240. Volume Two has 25 exams and four final Exams.
Book #237 - INSTRUCTORS GUIDE.

Item #111 - Tom Henry's 1993 Code Tabs. Have all the **KEY** Code References at your finger tips! A special row of service calculation tabs for both residential and commercial. 6 motor calculation tabs to size the wire, heaters, breakers, feeders, etc. to motors. Contains a total of 68 tabs.
Will fit all types of the N.E.C.

Book #107- Control Circuits. A "most requested" book to make control circuits easy to understand for the electrician that is unfamilar with controls. Circuits are drawn with pictures even showing the flow of voltage throughout the schematic. Order yours today!

Book #106 - "Above The Ceiling" Coming this Summer 1992. By Popular Request Tom Henry has made his 13th book on humor. Humor that has been collected from over 13,000 Electricians over the past 36 years! Hundreds of "one liners" with graphics.

Book #109 - How To Pass The Electrical Exam. Why take an electrical exam when you are not prepared and fail. Failing hurts, plus it's expensive re-taking exams. This book explains how to read, how to memorize and what to memorize. It breaks down each part of an exam and shows you exactly how to prepare for it. Now you can test yourself to see if you are prepared to take an exam.

Item #116- Formula Insert Pages. Tom Henry's 12 pages of calculation formulas and formats. Formulas for exact K, voltage drop, efficiency, ohms law, kva, transformers, ambient corrections, motor calculation steps, etc.... Pages are predrilled to fit the Looseleaf Code book. Excellent guide to have in your Code book.

Book #212 - BRAND NEW "REMINDERS for the Electrician" Book which contains the hard to remember load calculation formats, bus bar formulas, neutral balancing formulas, reversing connections of motors (split phase, capacitor, wound rotor, synchronous, etc.) transformer connections, dwelling formats, cooking equipment formats, switch connections, motor control connections, etc., etc.

Tom Henrys's **Code Electrical Classes Inc. & Bookstore**
6832 Hanging Moss Road Orlando, FL 32807
1-800-642-2633